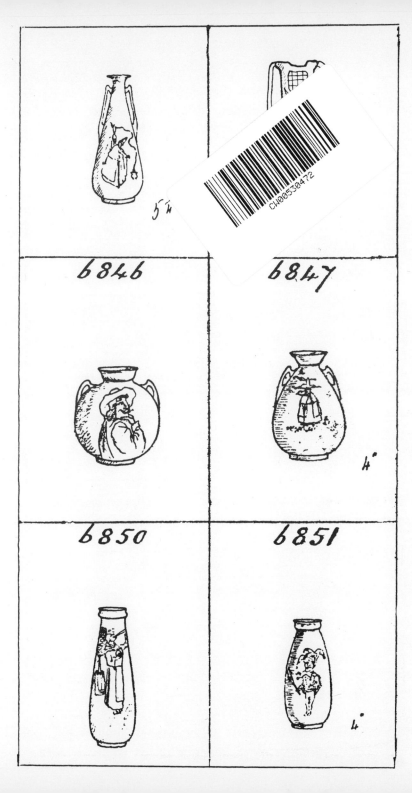

6846

6847

6850

6851

COLLECTING
DOULTON
KINGSWARE

1899–1940

**A COLLECTORS' LIST COMPILED BY
JOCELYN LUKINS**

Title page: *Night Watchman* clock 12" transfer printed *Peace* flagon, 7.5". Spirit Barrel with *Tavern* scenes. *Tony Weller* miniature flask and *Fagin* miniature jug.   *The Billings Collection.*

Ye 19th Hole ashtray. *Mr Pickwick* flask, *Golfers* matchball, *Coachman* 10.5", *MacCallum* jug. *Dame* tea caddy (wrong lid)   *Courtesy Phillips.*

Typesetting by Francis Salmon.

The products listed and shown were originally manufactured by Royal Doulton.
The names *Doulton* and *Royal Doulton* and the backstamps shown are registered trade marks.

© JOCELYN LUKINS 1992

ISBN 0 95 10288 5 5

PUBLISHED BY VENTA BOOKS

JOCELYN LUKINS photography Ventafile
The majority of photographs and illustrations in this book have been supplied by Ventafile, a compilation of material and information assembled by Jocelyn Lukins.

CONTENTS

Captain Phillip, Churchwarden, The Quiet Woman, Crown and *Tony Weller* flasks;
with *Don Quixote* jug 9" dated 1938 *Courtesy Phillips*

KINGSWARE is one of the most attractive and interesting of all the Doulton processes to collect. The characters which decorate it are full of charm and the number of flasks in particular are such that an enthusiastic collector can assemble the majority of them, yet leave the possibility of adding an elusive or previously unknown title or variation. When *Doulton Kingsware Whisky Flasks* was published in 1981 there were many gaps in the list which can be filled now. Perhaps in another ten years we may be able to complete it. In my 1981 price list a Kingsware flask, even a rarity, hardly ever cost more than one hundred pounds. In 1992 they can cost a thousand pounds. What will have happened by the year 2000, with more collectors and less Kingsware?

Throughout his brilliant career Charles Noke was always attempting experimental glazes such as his exotic *Chang* and *Chinese Jade*. Noke developed *Kingsware* from about 1898 after working on his *Holbein* wares. *Kingsware* was to use the same technique of Slip Painting but with a much more economical method which made a cheaper product. That is why we find the process used so much for advertising wares where a unit price for an issue of a thousand flasks for instance is important.

The process was unique to Doulton and never attempted by any other factory and impossible to reproduce today. Noke reversed the usual method of manufacture, by applying the colour, layer upon layer, to the inside of the embossed plaster of paris mould. The coloured body slip, usually terracotta, was then added and the whole thing fired in one operation so that the colours fused into the body. The effect is much softer than that achieved by standard methods. On the other hand the colours are consequently never very saturated and one rarely gets a bright red or green which gives a unique appearance. If you compare the Kingsware *Here's a Health Unto His Majesty* loving cup with its Aerographed brown counterpart where the colour has been added after the piece has left the mould in the usual and easier method, you can appreciate the subtle rich effect Kingsware has.

4

Queensware Queen Elizabeth I Jug 6.5" 1936.

QUEENSWARE was made by exactly the same process but using an ivory body was not as effective. It must be the brown base combined with the subdued brown, green and yellow slips which is so successful.

The first *Kingsware* designs were produced in the early years of the twentieth century. The *Watchman* design, one of Noke's creations, was used on Seriesware in the 1890's and adapted as an early Kingsware design in 1903. Many 'olde worlde' designs soon followed; *The Witch* and *Wizard*, *Alchemist* and *Monk*. All these designs are incised *Noke* and are the type of subjects he seemed to enjoy.

Desmond Eyles in *Doulton Burslem Wares* tells how *Charles Noke himself played a major part in the inspiration and design of many of the flagons, other designers including Harry Tittensor, Arthur Eaton, Leonard Langley and Harry Fenton, with a special mention of Arthur Bailey 1912-1932, a specialist in painting with slips who was responsible for painting the prototypes of many of the Kingsware flagons.*

Dickens was a favourite author of Charles Noke and many of Dicken's characters appear as Kingsware subjects. On the whisky flasks; a set of miniature vases and jugs; an impressive jug with the head of Charles Dickens acting as a spout and his characters around the body of the jug; as a Memories Jug and over a complete range of teaware. Eight different characters appear on the flasks (plus partners). Jesters and huntsmen, other favourite Noke subjects, appear throughout. Also used are subjects from history, legend and literature. Even more subjects are associated with the pleasures of drinking whisky, wine, ale and tea, and also of the smoking of tobacco. Subjects suitable to the use given to the wares.

As many of the flasks were intended as whisky containers they are often decorated with Scottish subjects.

FRED MOORE 1927-1957

Fred Moore spend much of his thirty years at Doulton Burslem working on Kingsware. Luckily before his death, when he was enjoying his retirement in Devon in 1982, he spoke to Louise Irvine and Marquerita Trevelyan-Clark of The *Royal Doulton International Collectors Club* and at the same time kindly wrote to me answering some of the queries I still had after compiling *Doulton Kingsware Whisky Flasks*.

In RDICC Magazine, volume three, number two, you can read the full interview, but this is what Fred Moore had to say about his life at Doulton, especially relating to Kingsware:-

I won a two year scholarship to the Burslem School of Art when I was thirteen and studied pottery design under the famous Gordon Forsyth. In 1927 when I was fifteen there was an opening at Doulton's and I was offered the chance of an apprenticeship. Gordon Forsyth obviously had great faith in me as before I had even started the job, he introduced me to the Lord Mayor of Stoke as the future Art Director of Doulton's. I never did realise that ambition although I did later reach that position at the W.H. Grindley Pottery. Forsyth's daughter Moira drew a portrait of me as I was about to embark on my new career at Doultons looking very young and innocent. Despite appearances I was still bold enough to immediately ask Arthur Bailey my new boss, what my wages were to be. He said he would speak to Mr Noke who took a very dim view of my query, believing I was privileged to have such a job and should be grateful for the honour alone. However, a sum was finally settled at 5 shillings a week. [25 pence].

I worked under Arthur Bailey and Arthur Eaton in the slip painting department which made all the Holbein, Rembrandt and Barbotine wares as well as the popular Kingswares. My first day's work was piping the raised lettering onto the Dame Kingsware teaset which featured an old lady drinking tea and the quotation 'The cup that cheers'. I would squeeze liquid slip through a glass nozzle, a bit like icing a cake, to create the lettering on this and all the other Kingsware designs, including the thousands of flasks for Dewars whisky.

Kingsware was at the peak of its popularity when I worked in the slip painting department and many extra hands from other departments were pulled in to cope with Dewar's special orders. In 1930, a huge commission meant that the department required two more full time decorators and a Mrs Hudson and the lady who was to become my wife joined the team. The Spanish Civil War in 1936 caused a slump in the demand for Kingsware as most of it had previously been exported to Spain. Perhaps collectors would find flasks out there!

Kingsware flasks are indeed found in Spain and there are many collectors there. Fred Moore goes on to describe the slip ware department in those days.

There was a very convivial atmosphere in the slip ware department caused mostly by Arthur Eaton's singing whilst he worked. He was a marvelous baritone and strains of Song of the Flea and other tunes would fill the room. The studio itself was very basic and absolutely filthy - the windows were only cleaned every two to three years and mice nibbled away at all the drawings. It was not uncommon to see rats running around outside. We all worked by gas light - the gas was produced on the factory and used to buzz incessantly as it came through the pipes. The only smart studio was C J Noke's which actually had a carpet. Until I was twenty-one all my work had to go up to this office for approval but apart from that I had little to do with the Art Director.

In his letter to me dated 21st December 1982 he says,

"KINGSWARE - from what I recall;

BACCHUS - The *Bacchus* flagon consisted of the figure of a man sitting astride a barrel. The whole thing being the container and the liquid was poured from his hat.

HOGARTH - I think the flagon you refer to in your book as *Churchwarden* is Hogarth. I do not recall ever painting this flagon but Arthur Bailey had a flagon in his possession which he told me was *Hogarth* and from what I remember it was the same as your illustration *Churchwarden*.

FORTY THIEVES - I do not recall a flagon under this name. The only article I painted was a round ashtray with a figure of *One of the Forty* standing in the centre. He wore a turban and pantaloons. The figure was modelled in the round.

HUNTSMAN FOX - This flagon is the one you portray on page 20 in your book. The head of the fox was the pouring spout and I think there were three or four hounds chasing across the back.

MENDOZA - I painted many of these flagons which were similar in shape to *He's a Jolly Good Fellow* in bare fist fighting stance. He was stripped to the waist and wore trousers which were fastened below the knee. There were several heads of spectators in the background similar to the heads around Dickens on *Memories* jugs.

Flagons I never painted and do not recall were - *Sam Weller, Drake* and *The Galleon, Haymarket* and *Ye Weary Pilgrim*.

I lettered many thousands of *Kingsware* items using a rubber bag with a glass tube attached. The bag was filled with 'slip' and the lettering was as you would ice a cake - The Cup That Cheers etc. etc."

Since that letter many of the queries have been solved. *Bacchus, The Forty Thieves, The Galleon* and *Mendoza* have all been found. *The Huntsman Fox* was explained by Fred Moore and the Doulton Catalogue page illustrates it on page 9 with that title. *Haymarket* has been found to be a *Dewars* Lambeth flask. Although *Sam Weller* appears with *Mr Pickwick* and *Drake* exists as a jug - they do not have flagons in their name. *Ye Weary Pilgrim* is still a mystery unless it is the beach scene issued by *Greenlees* in 1909 but I think this unlikely. At one time I thought it might be the lightheaded lady, *The Quiet Woman*, but I don't think so any longer. The letter tells us that *Mendoza* was a late flask as Fred Moore worked on it after 1927 and the *Forty Thieves* and the *Galleon* probably early ones before his time. Hogarth we know by a design number now, from the Doulton records D5597. Hogarth lived from 1697- 1764 when turbans were worn by men but never powdered wigs, so he probably never appeared as a flask but on numerous jugs and other objects.

Fred Moore mentions *Holbein* and *Rembrandt* wares. Here is a short explanation of the way in which they differ from Kingsware.

HOLBEIN 1895
Charles Noke developed glazes which gave the effect of 'old master' painting with application of slip in yellow, green and shades of brown on a cream earthenware body. The portraits were by Walter Nunn, Harry Tittensor, William Hodgkinson and others. This name was also given to a range of art nouveau flowing shapes for vases, loving cups and candlesticks again with coloured slips in the same colour range and almost in relief. There is a special mark but very similar pieces are found unmarked.

REMBRANDT 1989
Makes use of the same yellow, green and browns but the base is heavy marl. The thrown pots have surface so indented that the glaze has a rough appearance. The decoration incorporates portrait ovals taken from old master paintings with added calligraphy. The texts include *A Thing of beauty is a joy forever. Be content the sea hath fish enough* and others of a similar relaxing vein.

Rembrandt is sometimes impressed on the base but many pieces are unmarked. However it is easy to distinguish them from the Holbein pieces by observing the body. Production was small on these prestigious pieces.

Although not all *Rembrandt* and *Holbein* pieces are marked, *Rembrandt* can be distinguished by its body and surface striations, but there is a very thin line to be drawn between what is *Holbein* and what is *Kingsware*. The main difference was originally the price, which reflected the amount of work done. The vase on the right and the plaque on page 8, I classify as Holbein as they have a good colour range with careful detailing, they are more ambitious in finish than most Kingsware, and of limited production. I think I have the distinction correct, *Kingsware* was a mass-produced version of *Holbein* ware.

Richard Arkwright, Leather Bottle, & *Hooked* flasks with *In the Stocks* jug and *Holbien* vase.
The Billings Collection

Cavaliers Holbein plaque 11".

Dame teapot, *Mr Pickwick Proposes a Toast* flask & *Golfers* Tankard in aerographed brown finish. See page 44.

9

The preceding catalogue pages of KINGSWARE FLAGONS show many interesting details, two sizes of the *Don Quixote* flask, the miniatures and above all the interesting sales prices from 4/6 (22.5 pence) to a staggering 8/- (80 pence) for a moulded head version. Unfortunately the photographs are not dateable yet. The titles given are very casual throughout. *Watchman* is labelled *Bill Sykes* (an incorrect Doulton spelling), *The Pied Piper* becomes *Piper* in the first, while *Pipe Major* becomes *Highlander* in the second. Here *Sporting Squire* is *Squire Huntsman* and *Night Watchman* becomes *Old Watchman*. However, the other titles are helpful and one *Sailor's Story* allowed me to label correctly a flask I had wrongly designated in *Doulton Kingsware Whisky Flasks*. There are some useful design numbers. *Don Quixote* D4965 - 1929 gives the latest date on the top photograph. There are the same four Dewars subjects in both photographs which suggests these flasks were the pieces they had available on the studio shelves. If only Doulton had kept one copy of each piece issued and dated them as they do today.

Doulton Pattern Book showing designs submitted to Dewars No.1 'The Pipe Major' was selected and 720 ordered in the first instance, although a 1,000 has been mentioned as a minimum order. Notice that N.o.3 is very similar to the design *Rob Roy* issued to their competitors Greenlees in 1912!

A great number of Kingsware flasks were made by Doulton for JOHN DEWAR AND SONS of Perth, Scotland, a firm who also used Doulton's Lambeth stoneware flagons to contain and advertise its products. Many of the designs were exclusive to Dewars, but it was not unknown for some to be adapted for use elsewhere. Other firms supplied were *Bulloch Lade, Clan MacKenzie, Glenlivet & Co Ltd, Greenlees, H & A Dickens Whisky (Queensware), Hill Thompson* and *James Watson*. A full list appears on page 12.

KINGSWARE advertising flasks were usually issued in editions of one thousand, the minimum order required by Doulton, but some were recorded for many years and many thousands could have been produced of these titles. Popular subjects were reissued with different letter types and wording, and some have tube lined titles, others do not. Later flasks for Dewars had the brand name stamped on the base, a much cheaper method than the applied lettering, suggesting that Doulton were trying to keep within a budget, for Desmond Eyles recalls that the contract with Dewars stated that there would be no increase in price during the issue of the design over the years! We do not know the price agreed, but the retail price for an empty John Barleycorn flask in 1932 was seven shillings (35 pence).

DEWARS and other distillers and blenders sold the filled flasks in wine shops and off licenses. Christmas was a great time for trade as the contemporary advertisements show. The flasks were fastened with gilt paper seals and tartan ribbon. In Australia the Dewars flasks have been found with miniature diaries for 1936 attached. These prestigious containers were used very much in the export trade which explains why they are found spread so widely over the world. In fact some titles are rarely found in the United Kingdom. Rarities are more likely to be found in Australia, Canada or the United States.

Oyez! Oyez! flask with Diary for 1936 attached.

Micawber exists overprinted on the reverse. *Federal Law forbids sale or re-use of this bottle. Exporters Hudson's Bay Company, London, England.* The only flagon found with this designation. It was issued in an edition of 3,000. It had a slight variation in the design, the coat being given 10 buttons instead of the 12 found on the Dewar's flask. This seems to be one of the last Kingsware flasks to be issued and is one of the few pictured in Doulton's Design Book of Advertising Wares, as design number 358, dating it to 1938.

The design shows it was originally issued with a pottery stopper.

DISTILLERS AND WHISKY BLENDERS WHO COMMISSIONED FLASKS

Title		Ht.	Date
BULLOCH LADE	Pied Piper	8"	1904
	Gillie & Fisherman - John Hassall	8"	
	John Barleycorn	7"	1931
CLAN MACKENZIE	Watchman with modelled head	8"	1904
JOHN DEWAR	Admiral of the Fleet	7.5"	1918
	'Richard Arkwright'	9+"	1906
	Beefeater	7.25"	1908
	'Ben Jonson'	8"	1909
	'Bonnie Prince Charlie'	7"	1912
	'Captain Phillip'	7"	1938
	Churchwarden	10"	1906
	'The Connoisseur'	9"	1931
	The Crown	6"	1937
	'Micawber - The Ever Expectant'	7"	
	'Tony Weller - Beware of the Vidders'	8"	
	'Falstaff'	7.5"	1907
	'George the Guard'	10"	1909
	'George the Guard'	8"	
	'Here's a Health unto His Majesty'	9"	1936
	'Jovial Monk'	8"	1908
	'The Macnab'	9"	1915
	The Monk	8"	1904
	'Nelson' I	8"	1914
	'Nelson' II	8.5"	1935
	'Oyez Oyez'	10"	1909
	'Oyez Oyez'	9"	
	'The Pipe Major'	8"	1916
	'Sporting Squire'	8"	1909
	'Sporting Squire'	6"	1910
	'Sporting Squire'	6.5"	1911
	Uncle Sam	7.5"	1907
	Uncle Sam (Queensware)	7.5"	
	'Night Watchman'	10.5"	1902
	'Night Watchman'	7"	1902
GLENLIVET & CO	Pied Piper	8"	1904
GREENLEES BROS	Pirates	6.5"	1909
	'A Fish Story'	7"	1910
	'A State Governor - 100 Years Ago'	7"	1911
	'Tam o'Shanter pursued by the Witches'	7"	1911
	'Rob Roy'	8.5"	1912
	Crusader	8"	1913
	'Hooked' - John Hassall	6.5"	1914
H & A DICKENS	'Tony Weller' (Queensware)	8.25"	1936
	'Micawber'	7.25"	
	'Mr Pickwick from Dickens'	8.5"	1939
	'Mr Pickwick Proposes a Toast'	8"	
	'Stiggins'	8.5"	
HILL THOMPSON	'Micawber - The Ever Expectant'	7"	1938
JAMES WATSON	'Doctor Johnson at the Cheshire Cheese'	8"	1905

Titles in inverted commas appear in tube line or incised on the flask.

From the preceding list it can be seen that *Pied Piper* was overprinted for both *Bulloch Lade* and *Glenlivet* whiskeys. *Micawber* was issued to *Hill Thompson* slightly modified after being issued to *Dewars* for many years.

The *Hill Thompson Hudson Bay Company, Micawber* is a late flask being issue in 1938 when Doulton designs were better recorded. We are told it was made in an issue of 3,000 and yet I regard this as a comparatively rare flask. I have not sold many but perhaps there are more found in North America? It makes me think that most jugs were made in many thousands. For instance *Captain Phillip*, it is stated, was made in an issue of one thousand only and yet it is not rare. One Australian collector had six in his collection as he said none of them were quite the same! Which is of course true of *Kingsware*, being handmade and the final result rather unpredictable.

STOPPERS

Many flasks have a rounded hallmarked silver stopper and chain attaching them to the handle by a ring. These were made as prestigious decanters to be sold with or without contents in department stores. The stoppers made in London were probably fitted outside the Doulton factory.

Dewars flasks were fitted with nickel plated brass stoppers with the word *Dewars* embossed twice on a plain ball stopper.

Dewars - Crown had a special brass crown stopper embossed *Dewars*.

Dewars - Captain Phillip had a special coppered ship stopper embossed *Dewars*.

Dewars - Here's a Health Unto His Majesty is often found with a thistle stopper which could be the original supplied.

Greenlees stoppers were similar to *Dewars* ball type but without lettering.

H & A Dickens whisky had special globular pottery stoppers.

Bulloch Lade and Hill Thompson flasks were also issued with pottery stoppers.

Reproduction stoppers have been made in Australia for some years and in view of the lack of originals, I think this quite acceptable in a collection. However, to my knowledge *Kingsware* flasks never originally carried the *Dewars Imperial Whisky elaborate stoppers sometimes seen. The reproductions are easily detectable as they are usually heavier and made in one piece. The original Dewars ball stoppers are in two parts, the ball being attached to the cork by a screw.*

DOULTON produced their own line of *Kingsware* flasks with silver fittings. These never have a brand name and were prestige products sold by retailers, such as *Maple & Company* of London, who advertised in 1905. *A whisky flagon amounts to 14s.6d. and is of quaint shape and cheerful expression, it makes a suitable present for a man.* The illustration shows a *Fisherman* flask and alongside it, in the same *Kingsware* design, a Loving Cup, an Ashtray and a Matchstriker all silver mounted.

Many flasks were probably available only for one year, certainly the rarer ones including the *Greenlees* flasks. Some were issued to commemorate special occasions: the Coronation of George V and Queen Mary in 1911 (*Sporting Squire*), the proposed Coronation of Edward VIII in 1936 (*Here's a Health unto His Majesty*), the Coronation of George VI and Queen Elizabeth in 1937 (*The Crown*), the Sesquicentenary of the Settlement of New South Wales in 1938 (*Captain Phillip*).

The Commemorative jug, tankard and Matchstriker made for the 1911 Coronation were probably made in small quantities as they appear so infrequently. The transfer printed *Dewars* flask issued in 1919 to commemorate the end of the First World War, however, seems to have been a large run, no doubt because the world had such a lot of celebrating to do.

Something Different

A whisky of proved worth in an attractive Doulton-ware flagon - here is a unique and lasting gift which has been introduced by Dewar's. There are twelve different shapes which contain the same quality as each bottle of "White Label" whisky, and each flagon costs 17s. 6d.

(2) Van Harding shirts, with button-on Van Heusen semi-stiff collars and detachable cuffs, are a welcome gift. The familiar White Label whisky may come to us this Christmas in quaint Doulton-ware flagons, as shown in the illustration.

A Doulton-ware flagon of Dewar's whisky

A splendid whisky in a Doulton-ware flagon decorated with a quaint traditional figure—Dewar's White Label

The Bystander 17.12.1930

Stop Press

Extract from London Office Memo letter of 24/10/30

DOULTONWARE FLAGONS. We will prepare and send you ten half cases of Doultonware Flagons. Five of the cases will contain the following six designs of flagons:-

Tony Weller	Jovial Monk
George the Guard	Ben Johnson
Prince Charlie	Macnab

and the other five will contain the following six designs.-

Crier	Falstaff
Sporting Squire	Watchman
Micawber	Pipe Major

So that in the event of a customer having one half and ordering a second half, you will be able to send him a complete set of twelve. The first named half set will be numbered "1" on the end of the case, and the second named section will be numbered "2" on the end of the cases.

This information received from John Dewar regarding supplies to their retailers confirms my deductions on page 15.

A study of contemporary Dewars advertisements can tell us which flasks were in the range in particular years. Most of the advertisements appear in the Christmas issues, the gift season.

BRITANIA & EVE	December 1929 *(see page 17)*	
Falstaff	*The MacNab*	*Sporting Squire*
1907-1930	1915-1930	1909-1930
THE SPHERE	November 29th 1930 *(See page 14)*	
Oyez! Oyez!	*Falstaff*	*The MacNab*
1909-1930	1907-1930	1915-1930
THE GRAPHIC	December 15th 1930	
Tony Weller	-1930	
THE BYSTANDER	December 17th 1930	
Night Watchman	1903-1930	

Notice all these flasks were issued with the standard Dewars ball stopper and a trim of tartan ribbon. They contained White Label whisky (Dewars export blend) and in 1930 cost 17/6 (87.5 pence), in 1905 they were 14/6 (72.5 pence) inflation wasn't so rapid in those days. Twelve different shapes, which probably meant subjects available, are mentioned in *The Sphere* advert. This would explain the relatively common Dewars flasks. The six subjects shown here and perhaps the other six would be:-

Micawber	-1930	*George the Guard*	1908-1930
Ben Jonson	1909-1930	*The Jovial Monk*	1908-1930
Bonnie Prince Charlie	1912-1930	*The Pipe Major*	1916-1930

Unfortunately records are sparse, neither Doulton nor Dewar's realised, perhaps, how extremely collectable these flasks would become and of how much interest in the future.

The following list of whisky flasks has now been expanded to include 64 different titles plus 30 different shapes and variations of lettering. With the 11 Queensware listed and six overglaze decorated versions that makes a total of 111 to be collected, so far. That is not including the "Green" versions and the many colour variations. It does not include esoteric variations like the *Watchman* with modelled head flask found with a transfer of *Bill Sikes Bullseye* on it! Or the *Pipe Major* with added moustache where some enthusiastic painter has attempted to sharpen up a few details after the piece has left the mould. Pupils are added to eye sockets sometimes but I think the designs are much better without these crude afterthoughts.

When you leave the flasks and collect jugs, vases and tableware etc. the variations in shape and decoration are innumerable. I have not attempted to list all of these. For one thing I have not yet seen all of the ones illustrated in the Doulton Design books and there are always even more which can come to light, which for some unaccountable reason were not recorded. The design books were a painters guide to the colours used and therefore it is not always stated if the design was for a flask or a jug or both. With the list of flasks perhaps we are nearing completion. I know several collectors around the world who have almost all the present known titles but none who have them all and they are never missing the same ones. The rarest are of course the special Doulton presentation decanters. I only know of one copy of the *Jester* and the *Forty Thieves* but I am sure *Fox Hunting* and *Grouse Shooting*, of which I also know only one copy at the moment, must have been popular subjects and, like *The Quiet Woman*, flask will perhaps emerge to find their way to the collections in number. There must be other titles still to find which makes the search exciting. Thank you to everyone who has helped in the search;

Ron Bahn, Lester Barrett, Derek and Kay Billings, Bill Dickson, Katherine Ellis, *Royal Doulton Archives*, Louise Irvine, Pete Jackman, Tony Lalor, Joe and Viv Medlyn, George Mosinho, Elizabeth Nevell, Mark Oliver *(Phillips)*, Mr and Mrs L R Robinson, Robin Keiller, *John Dewar & Sons (United Distillers)*, David Westcott.

TITLES OF FLASKS

ADMIRAL OF THE FLEET - Dewars
THE ALCHEMIST
"RICHARD ARKWRIGHT" - Dewars
"ARTFUL DODGER & OLIVER TWIST" (2)
BACCHUS OR MAN ON A BARREL
BEEFEATER   - Dewars
"BEN JOHNSON" -Dewars
BILL SIKES
"BONNIE PRINCE CHARLIE" - Dewars
"CAPTAIN PHILLIP" - Dewars
CHABAND
CHURCHWARDEN
COACHMAN
"THE CONNOISSEUR"
THE CROWN - Dewars
CRUSADER - Greenlees
DICK TURPIN
"DON QUIXOTE & SANCHO PANCA (2)
"FAGIN"
"FALSTAFF" - Dewars
"A FISH STORY' - Greenlees
FISHERMAN
THE FORTY THIEVES
FOX HUNTING
THE GALLEON
"GEORGE THE GUARD" - Dewars (2)
GILLIE & FISHERMAN - Bulloch Lade
GOLFERS
GROUSE SHOOTING
"HERE'S A HEALTH UNTO HIS MAJESTY -Dewars
"HE'S A JOLLY GOOD FELLOW
"HOOKED" - Greenlees
HUNTSMAN FOX
JESTER

JOHN BARLEYCORN & variations
DOCTOR JOHNSON - Watsons
"THE JOVIAL MONK" - DEWARS (2)
LEATHER BOTTLE
"THE MACNAB" - Dewars
"MEMORIES"
MENDOZA
MICAWBER
THE MONK
"NELSON" I - Dewars
"NELSON" II - Dewars
"OYEZ! OYEZ!" - Dewars
"MR PICKWICK"
"MR PICKWICK FROM DICKENS" - H&A
"MR PICKWICK PROPOSES"
"PIED PIPER" & var.
"THE PIPE MAJOR" - Dewars & var
PIRATES - Greenlees
THE QUIET WOMAN
ROB ROY - Greenlees
A SAILORS STORY
"SPORTING SQUIRE" - Dewars
"A "STATE GOVERNOR" - Greenlees
'STIGGINS'
TAM O'SHANTER" - Greenlees
TAVERN SCENES
SPIRIT BARRELS
"TONY WELLER" -Dewars
TONY WELLER FIGURAL
UNCLE SAM - Dewars
NIGHT WATCHMAN - Dewars & var
WATCHMAN WITH MODELLED HEAD
WIZARD

WHO SAYS DEWAR'S?

Could you imagine a more timely and welcome gift for any whisky-wise friend than one of these special Dewar's flagons? The shape and design are so attractive, so unusual, the lustre of the famous Doulton ware so rich and deep and the whisky inside—Dewar's "White Label"—is one of the finest things that ever came out of Scotland! There are twelve entirely different patterns to choose from and each holds one-sixth of a gallon. Your usual supplier can give you full particulars and will show you the complete range of flagons.

ADMIRAL OF THE FLEET
7.5" high. Rd. No. 660262 1918. DEWAR'S on the reverse.

ADMIRAL BEATTY was commander-in-Chief Grand Fleet from 1916 to 1919 during the First World War. In 1916, Beatty, with his battle cruisers, shown here in the background, was engaged in a great sea fight with the Germans off Jutland. His success made him a national hero and he was granted an Earldom in 1919.

THE ALCHEMIST
8" high. Rd. No. 435890 1904 Incised Noke.

MANY people of all classes, including Kings, philosophers and clergy dabbled in alchemy from the 12th to 17th centuries. They sought the Philosophers' Stone which would transmute baser metals into gold, the Elixir of Life which would prolong life indefinitely and the Alkahest or universal solvent. Although misdirected to such impossible ends, their experiments resulted in many valuable discoveries in the true sciences.

"RICHARD ARKWRIGHT"
9" high. Rd. No. 471183 1906. DEWAR'S WHITE LABEL WHISKY on base. D 86

"RICHARD ARKWRIGHT 1732-1792" appears on the face and "INVENTOR OF THE SPINNING FRAME" appears on the reverse of the flask in gold.

SIR RICHARD ARKWRIGHT, English inventor who perfected the first practical mechanical cotton spinning machine in 1769. At first worked with animal power, he adapted his machine to water power in 1771, and steam in 1790. His mill at Cromford, Derbyshire was a wonder of the age and he became the inventor of mass production and one of the first capitalists.

"THE ARTFUL DODGER & OLIVER TWIST

from *Oliver Twist* by Charles Dickens.

Two versions exist, 7" and 8" high. The 7" globular version exists with silver mount dated 1928 at the base, incised *Noke* and *The Artful Dodger and Oliver Twist* on the reverse.

JOHN DAWKINS, nicknamed The Dodger, a member of Fagin's young gang of pickpockets, enlists Oliver Twist when he meets him on his arrival in London. *He was altogether, as roistering and swaggering a young gentleman as ever stood four feet six, or something less, in his bluchers.*

BACCHUS or Man on a Barrel

8.5" figural flask.

BACCHUS was the Roman God of wine. Doulton's title for this flask seems to me rather inappropriate. Since the eighteenth century and Ralph Wood the English have produced a traditional toby with a figure astride a barrel, sometimes called the *Landlord Flask*. Lambeth produced this type in the nineteenth and twentieth century (Harry Simeon) and this is a Burslem *Kingsware* version.

BEEFEATER

7.25" high. Rd. No. 527012. 1908.

Incised Noke. On the reverse DEWAR'S SCOTCH WHISKY.

BEEFEATER is a popular name given to the Yeoman Warders of the Tower of London. It is a corruption of *Buffetiers*, which was a body of foot guards formed in the reign of Henry VII, 1485-1509, for the protection of the Royal Person. They still perform this duty on ceremonial occasions and still wear the dress style of the Tudor period.

19

"BEN JONSON"
7" high. R. No. 543367. 1909.

Occurs with or without the title on the front and DEWAR'S SCOTCH WHISKY on the reverse, also the type of lettering differs and DEWAR'S is sometimes printed on the base as it was made over a long period. Early examples only signed *Noke*.

BEN JONSON, 1573-1637, soldier, player, playwright and poet, was a contemporary and friend of Shakespeare. As a man he was arrogant and quarrelsome, he once killed a fellow actor, but was fearless and warm hearted too. Essentially the first Poet Laureate, he is buried in Westminster Abbey.

BILL SIKES
from *Oliver Twist* by Charles Dickens

7.25" high. Rd. No. 453403. 1905.

A flask with a modelled head representing Bill Sikes glowering countenance with a transfer of his faithful bull terrier *"Bullseye"* on the reverse. A green version of this flask exists.

BILL SIKES was a brutal thief associated with Fagin, and the lover and murderer of Nancy who aided Oliver's escape. He finally hangs himself accidentally whilst trying to escape the mob hunting him down.

A stoutly built fellow of about five and thirty......a broad heavy countenance with a beard of three days' growth and two scowling eyes, one of which displayed various parti-coloured symptoms of having been damaged by a blow.

"BONNIE PRINCE CHARLIE"
7" high. Rd. No. 618840. 1912. Title on front. Variations of DEWAR'S, DEWAR'S WHISKY on reverse or DEWAR's on base. This flask was made over a long period.

CHARLES EDWARD STUART 1720-1788. The Young Pretender, grandson of James II of England and leader of the *Jacobites*, made the final and unsuccessful attempt in the 1745 rebellion to restore the Stuarts to the English throne. Charles, seen here in Highland dress, landed in Scotland and, with a faithful following of Highlanders, marched south into England. After some successes they were finally defeated at Culloden, but the much loved young man escaped to Europe with the help of his many Royal followers typified by Flora MacDonald.

"CAPTAIN PHILLIP"

7.25 high. DEWARS on the base. Special anchor stopper.

Ovoid flask showing Captain Phillip on the face and the sailing ship *Sirius* on the reverse. One thousand were issued in 1938 in commemoration of the Sesquincentenary of the foundation of the settlement of New South Wales and the City of Sydney.

CAPTAIN ARTHUR PHILLIP, Navigator, 1736-1814, left Portsmouth, England, in May 1787 and arrived at Botany Bay, Australia, in January 1788. Eleven ships carried 800 convicts, 200 - 300 officials, guards and free settlers. Due to the loss of the American colonies, a new outlet was sought for Britain's convicts. A site was chosen and Captain Phillip became Governor of New South Wales until 1792, by which time 5,000 convicts had cleared the site, laid the foundations and built Sydney.

"CHADBAND"
from *Bleak House* By Charles Dickens

An 8" high flask showing the Reverend gentleman in a drawing room interior, with an aspidistra in a window setting on the reverse.

The Reverend Mister Chadband, a hypocritical clergyman, a large yellow man, with a fat smile and a general appearance of having a good deal of train oil in his system. Mr Chadband moves softly and cumbrously, not unlike a bear who has been taught to walk upright.

CHURCHWARDEN

9.75" high. Rd. No. 486689. 1906. DEWAR'S SCOTCH WHISKY on reverse.

The long, curved stem pipe seen here was an early 19th century invention, named for the dignified lay administrators of the church, but fashionable with all. Clay pipes were provided for patrons by the tavern fireside and burnt clean there after use.

COACHMAN

A figural flagon with removable head. 10.5" high.

In the Doulton price list of 1932 it cost 8s.6d. (42 pence). A miniature version 5.5" high occurs. The head removes and there is sometimes a silver rim at the neck, 1908. The head is moulded in one with the stopper which is sometimes broken and replaced by a cork.

THE COACHMEN were the heroes of their age. Usually portrayed as roisterous daring fellows who undertook the then hazardous journeys across country with passengers and mail. Their many caped coats protected them from the weather.

"THE CONNOISSEUR"

9" HIGH. Ovoid flask. Title beneath the portrait. C. 1909.

CONNOISSEUR - an expert judge in matters of taste, the reference here being obviously to the taste for wine or spirits, for it shows a gentleman expertly studying the quality of the wine in his glass.

THE CROWN

6" high. 950 issued in 1937 to commemorate the Coronation of George VI. It has a special crown shaped stopper with DEWAR'S on it, DEWAR'S appears on the base and there is a laurel wreath handle. D353

ST EDWARD'S CROWN, the Imperial Crown of Great Britain and the one with which the sovereign is crowned. It was made during the reign of Charles II, 1660-1685, to replace an earlier one destroyed in the Civil War, said to have been worn by Edward the Confessor, 1042-1066. It is used at the Coronation and at the State Opening of Parliament. At other times it is displayed at the Tower of London.

CRUSADER

8 " high. Rd. No. 625349. 1913. AC 1913 on the reverse and GREENLEES BROS. CLAYMORE SCOTCH WHISKY DISTILLERS on the base.

CRUSADERS were engaged in the military expeditions undertaken by European nations for over two centuries, from 1095-1271. Their object was to keep the Christian shrines in the Holy Land out of Muslim control and to safeguard visiting pilgrims.

DICK TURPIN

8" high. A flask with a modelled head of Dick Turpin in a tri-corn hat has a ring stopper and chain as did all similar flasks.

DICK TURPIN (1706-1739) - an infamous highwayman who was finally arrested for horse stealing and hanged at York. Legend has transformed him into a romantic figure, dashing through the night on his horse "Black Bess".

"DON QUIXOTE".

Occurs in two sizes, a 10.5" and 9.75" high. Both unusually of an identical shape, a cylindrical flask with an angular handle (see page 9) D4965 =1929. Don Quixote and Sancho Panza on the face and on the reverse a horse and a donkey by a skeletal tree. The Don with a shield and a spear.

DON QUIXOTE was published by Cervantes in 1605 and was a burlesque on the romances of chivalry. Don Quixote is a poor gentleman of La Manche in Spain. An amiable character, he imagines himself called upon to roam the world in search of adventure on his old horse Rosinante, accompanied by a squire, the rustic Sancho Panza.

23

"FAGIN"

from *Oliver Twist* by Charles Dickens

8.24" high. Silver stopper and chain. 1908.

FAGIN was a receiver of stolen goods and leader of the gang of young thieves in the London underworld into which Oliver Twist was introduced.

A very old shrivelled Jew, whose villainous-looking and repulsive face was obscured by a quantity of matted red hair.

"FALSTAFF"

7.5" flattened circular flask with elongated handle. Rd. No. 508037. 1907.

Occurs with and without title, and sometimes with DEWAR'S SCOTCH WHISKY or DEWAR'S WHISKY on the reverse, or DEWAR'S on the base. Versions with either green or brown hat. D100.

SIR JOHN FALSTAFF appears in Shakespeare's *Henry IV* and *The Merry Wives of Windsor* - a fat, witty, good humoured knight, loving jests, self indulgent and over-addicted to sack.

"A FISH STORY"

7" high. Title tube lined on the face. On the reverse AC 1910 and on the base GREENLEES CLAYMORE SCOTCH WHISKY DISTILLERS.

The scene shows two gentlemen in eighteenth-century dress smoking and drinking, and yarning in a cosy tavern setting, with a large fish in a glass case on the wall above.

FISHERMAN

7" large globular flask with silver stopper and chain. 1904. Incised *Noke*. Fisherman in Sou'wester on the face and Herring Drifterson the reverse. Pale "greenish" copies occur but have the normal terracotta base making this just a colour variation.

A FISHERMAN and fishing vessels typical of the East Coast of Great Britain, from whose ports they went out to fish the shoals of herring in the North Sea, pitting wits and strength against the elements.

THE FORTY THIEVES

6" pear shaped flask. Showing a border of thieves at the base which correspond to the *One of the Forty* models in the figurine range. (See ashtrays). A rare flask incised *Noke*.

ALI BABA AND THE FORTY THIEVES is an oriental tale of unknown source, not originally part of the *Arabian Nights*. It tells the tale of Ali Baba and his enemies, the forty thieves, who concealed themselves in large wine jars in Ali Baba's house but were discovered by his servant girl, Morgiana, who killed them all by pouring boiling oil into the jars.

FOX HUNTING

7" flask showing mounted huntsman and hounds on the front and a cheeky fox sitting on the reverse. A subject found on many Kingsware shapes but the whisky flask is very rare.

FOX HUNTING is still practiced in Great Britain but I hope that it will soon, as bear and bull baiting and cock fighting have become, part of a colourful but rather disgraceful past.

THE GALLEON

8" globular flask modelled on the body in relief to show a galleon with red sails.

Silver stopper and chain.

THE GALLEON was a Spanish ship of war. Drake defeated the Spanish Armada in 1588 with a fleet of much smaller ships. The galleons were used to carry the wealth of the Americas home to Spain.

"GEORGE THE GUARD"

Occurs in two versions, both titled: a tall cylindrical form 10" high, and a pear shaped one 8.25" high. Both designs Rd. No. 545291. 1909. Both titled on face and DEWAR'S SCOTCH WHISKY or DEWAR'S WHISKY found on the reverse on the larger size. Incised *Noke*. D122.

A GUARD, like the one pictured here with a tricorn hat and a blunderbuss, was often carried on the mail coaches to protect the contents. The mail coaches were the fastest and most reckless on the road.

GILLIE AND FISHERMAN

8" high. On the reverse *BL Scotch High Ball* and *Bulloch Lade & Co Limited, Edinburgh*. This flask was fitted with a globular pottery stopper.

These characters are based on a caricature by John Hassal which appeared as an advert for Bulloch Lade. The fisherman is eyeing with envy his companion who is pouring "a wee dram" from a hip flask. *Hooked* is also based on a John Hassal cartoon.

GOLFERS

8.5" high. Issued in 1930.

In the board room at Dewar House there was a *Golfers* flask. With a label on the base stating that 200 were purchased by Dewar. A rather interesting fact gleaned as this design was not made for them.

GOLF is still a game of great antiquity and of Scottish origin, where there are still some internationally known courses. The game, here portrayed as being playing in 17th century dress, still remains remarkably popular, especially in Britain and the United States.

GROUSE SHOOTING

A 7" flask. Discovered for the first time in 1990 in the UK. One man aims at some flying birds, another and two dogs wait for the grouse to fall. On the reverse three grouse fly low over the Scottish moors.

THE RED GROUSE is a bird of the high British moorlands and it occurs in no other part of the world. It lives on the seeds and shoots of Heather. The bird shelters in the Heather and rarely flies, hence the use of beaters to drive it into the line of guns. When disturbed it flies low with whirring and gliding arched wings. The shooting season starts on the "Glorious Twelfth" in August and runs until December 10th. The two dogs are Spaniels trained to retrieve the birds when shot down.

"HERE'S A HEALTH UNTO HIS MAJESTY"

9" high. Title on the face. DEWAR'S on base. Issued in 1936 in an Edition of 900. Special thistle shaped stopper. D342.

A ROYALISTS' TOAST to their King at the time of the Civil War (1642-1646) and the first line of a song of that name. The flask shows a Cavalier in ostrich-plumed hat, making the toast. Issued in anticipation of the Coronation of Edward VIII which, because of the Abdication, was postponed to become that of George VI in May 1937.

"HE'S A JOLLY GOOD FELLOW"

A globular flask 8" high with silver fittings.

Issued in 1923 in an edition of 900.

This title, which appears on the flagon beneath a picture of six men drinking in a tavern, is the line of a celebratory chorus usually sung as a toast. The dress is 18th century and very reminiscent of Dr Johnson and his circle of companions.

"HOOKED"

6.5" flask with this title on the face. On the reverse AC 1914 and on the base, *Greenlees Claymore Scotch Whisky Distillers*. This subject is also from a drawing by John Hassall and is in his unique style and probably occurs as an advertisement for *Greenlees*. It shows a fisherman sitting on a wall having just hooked a fish in the water below. Does anyone know of the original illustration?

HUNTSMAN FOX

6.75" flask with a crouching fox on the top, the brush forming the handle.

On the face is the image of the *Sporting Squire*. Huntsman Fox was used by Doulton as a title for a very appealing animal model HN 100 showing a fox in hunting pink. A 10.5" flask occurs in the tableware series *Reynard the Fox*.

THE JESTER

A rare 6.25" flask with silver stopper and chain. Incised *Noke*.

THE JESTER was a subject very popular with Charles Noke so it was predictable that it would occur as a flask. His many other versions appear as figurines, masks, seriesware and character jugs. A figurine by Noke first designed and issued in 1892 is still in the current range giving it a production of 100 years at Burslem.

JOHN BARLEYCORN

A globular flask with asymmetrical neck, 7" high. Incised *Noke*. Issued 1913. Silver fittings and *art nouveau* borders. In 1931 it cost 3s.6d. (17.5 pence).

JOHN BARLEYCORN, shown here in 18th century dress with jug in hand, surrounded by ears of barley, is the personification of barley, the grain from which malt liquor is made. A version exists with BL on the reverse for *Bulloch Lade Scotch Whisky*.

DOCTOR JOHNSON

A Flask 8.25" high. Issued 1905. *Watsons Scotch Whisky* tube lined on the reverse. This is the only Kingsware flask made for this distiller.

SAMUEL JOHNSON published a dictionary of the English language in 1755; a prolific writer whose circle of friends included many of the most brilliant figures of his age. He is shown here with two companions in one of the many London taverns they frequented.

29

"THE JOVIAL MONK"

Rd. No. 527013. 1908. This flask occurs in two shapes, with or without the title and DEWAR'S. A round flattened flask, 7.75" high and a pear shaped flask, 8" high. D124

MONKS are very often associated with drinking, and monasteries have always been renowned for their brewing and distilling.

LEATHER BOTTLE

6.25" high x 6" long. This flask takes the form of a leather bottle, complete with simulated stitching, and has a silver stopper and chain, hallmarked 1919. On the side it shows a serving woman filling a row of leather bottles from a cask, whilst a man in Elizabethan dress drinks from one. On the reverse it shows a workman drinking from a similar bottle balanced on his arm.

Before the use of stoneware and, later, glass containers, tarred leather was a material used to contain, and from which to drink, ales, wines and spirits. A leather bottle was in former times hung as a sign outside a public house to show travellers that they could find refreshment there. Dickens in *Pickwick Papers* refers to a hostelry of that name, *The Leather Bottle* at Cobham, Kent, which remains practically unchanged since those days, and one can still be shown *'the room where Mr Pickwick slept'*.

"THE MACNAB"

Tall oval flask, 9" high. Issued in 1915. Occurs with or without the title, and with either DEWAR'S or DEWARS SCOTCH WHISKY on the reverse.

This subject was taken from a portrait owned by John Dewar & Sons Limited. It was painted in 1810 by Sir Henry Raeburn, R A, who was born and worked in Edinburgh. He exhibited the painting at the Royal Academy in 1819. It was bought by Lord Dewar in 1917 for 24,200 pounds and it hung in Dewar House, Haymarket, London until it closed in 1987. It is a portrait of Francis MacNab, who became 12th Laird of the MacNabs in 1778. The MacNabs fought on the side of the English at the Bannockburn in 1314, and afterwards forfeited their estates to the Dewars and the MacGregors. The portrait now hangs in the offices of *United Distillers*, Edinburgh..

"MEMORIES"

Tall pear shaped flask, 9" high, with six portraits. Issued in 1906. Memories is incised on the reverse with a further two portraits. There are four versions of this subject on Kingsware, all with a central figure lost in thought and surrounded by the friends he is calling to mind, but only the version shown here occurs on a flask, the other three are on water jugs.

"MENDOZA"

7.5" flask. Incised on the reverse *Mendoza*.

DANIEL MENDOZA was a Jewish prizefighter often commemorated in early 19th century ceramics, where he was usually shown engaged in his most famous fight with Humphries at Odiham, Hampshire, in 1788. He won the English Championship in 1792.
This was bare knuckle fighting.

MICAWBER

from *David Copperfield* By Charles Dickens.

7" high. "Micawber the Ever Expectant" beneath the portrait, DEWAR'S on the base. We have no introduction date for this flask, but it was a popular subject and sold in great numbers over a long period. A non *Dewars* version exists with five buttons. A version exists with *Dewars Imperial Whisky* printed in black on the reverse, it was also made for *Hill Thompson* (see page 11) and in Queensware and airbrush brown finish as shown here.

WILKINS MICAWBER, with whom David lodges on first coming to London, moves optimistically from employment to employment endeavouring to support his wife and ever increasing family. He is hopelessly improvident, but always confident that *something will turn up*. He remains David's staunch friend and unmasks the villainous Uriah Heep.

THE MONK

Tall flask, 8' high, with silver fittings. Rd. No. 435658. 1904. DEWAR'S on the base. Incised *Noke*. This MONK is in the cellar of a monastery sampling the wines stored there. This design was used on other Kingsware articles as early as 1902. The semi-circular window appears on many Kingsware flasks.

NELSON

Two distinct types with, unusually, different portraits on each. Flattened oviform flask. 8.5" high. Rd. No. 649343. 1914. Triangular flask. 8" high x 6" wide. DEWAR'S on reverse. D326 = 1935.

ADMIRAL LORD NELSON, 1758-1805, notable for his victories at the Nile, 1798, Copenhagen, 1801, and Trafalgar, 1805, where he was killed to be mourned by a whole nation as a popular hero. Notorious also for his love of Emma Hamilton, which has caught the romantic interest of writers ever since.

"OYEZ! OYEZ!"

Two shapes, an 8" oval flask and a 10" ewer shape. Rd. No. 545292. 1909. Incised *Noke*. DEWAR'S SCOTCH WHISKY on the reverse and DEWAR'S WHISKY on the base.

Before the days of cheap printing and news sheets and newspapers making news available to all, the town crier was the means of spreading information. He first rang his bell to attract a crowd and cried, 'Oyez! Oyez!', which is a Norman French word meaning 'Hear, Ye!'.

'MR PICKWICK

rom *Pickwick Papers* by Charles Dickens

" oviform flask shows Mr Pickwick in a characteristic
ose with his hands beneath his coat-tails in an interior
which, in this case, must represent the Fleet Prison where
e was imprisoned for debt. On the reverse is another
igure shown in the same setting, with incised title
eneath, "Sammy Vel". Sam, his faithful servant, caused
imself to be imprisoned so that he could rejoin his
master. Incised *Noke*. A second design "MR PICKWICK
PROPOSES A TOAST occurs in two shapes 7" and 8"
igh. Incised *Noke*. This shows the beginning of the story
vith Mr Pickwick standing and proposing a toast to
ther, seated, members of the *Pickwick Club*.

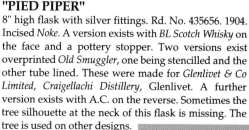

AMUEL PICKWICK was Founder Member and
President of the *Pickwick Club*. Created in the cause of
cientific and cultural matters, it becomes the vehicle for
 series of amusing adventures entered into by its
members. *Pickwick Papers* was Dickens' first novel, 1836.

harle Noke was a Dickens enthusiast and there is a third
esign,

MR PICKWICK FROM DICKENS, made for *H & A
Dickens Whisky* in the *Queensware* range. 8.5", 1939.

"PIED PIPER"

8" high flask with silver fittings. Rd. No. 435656. 1904.
Incised *Noke*. A version exists with *BL Scotch Whisky* on
the face and a pottery stopper. Two versions exist
overprinted *Old Smuggler*, one being stencilled and the
other tube lined. These were made for *Glenlivet & Co
Limited, Craigellachi Distillery*, Glenlivet. A further
version exists with A.C. on the reverse. Sometimes the
tree silhouette at the neck of this flask is missing. The
tree is used on other designs.

HE PIED PIPER OF HAMELIN' is a poem by
obert Browning based on an old legend from a
wn in Brunswick. In 1376 the town is overrun
y rats, and the mayor and corporation engage a
ranger to rid them of the vermin. This he does
y playing his pipe so sweetly that the rats follow
e music and drown in the River Weser. The
wnspeople refuse to pay the thousand guilders
ey promised as a fee. The strange piper plays
gain, but this time all the children of the town
llow him and disappear forever.

'THE PIPE MAJOR'

8.5" high. Title on the face. DEWAR'S on the base. Issued 1910. A non DEWARS flask with AC on the reverse exists in some numbers.

In Scotland the "pipes" referred to are the bagpipes. The pipes traditionally play the Scottish regiments into battle, and the flask shows an army pipe major with bagpipes and in full regalia.

THE PIRATES

6" flask with overhead handle. AC on the reverse and 1909. Printed on the base is GREENLEES BROTHERS CLAYMORE SCOTCH WHISKY DISTILLERS. Incised *Noke*.

Two sailors in seventeenth century dress pause for a yarn whilst unloading casks on the beach. A companion stands by with a musket, and offshore is a ship under full sail. Could this be *Ye Weary Pilgrim*?

THE QUIET WOMAN

6.5" flask. Two versions exist, one with the spout at the side as here, another with the aperture at the neck.

THE QUIET WOMAN is the name of a pub in Leek Staffordshire, there are, or were, others called The Good Woman, The Silent Woman and even The Headless Woman, all showing a woman carrying her head in her hands. Originally this image probably referred to decapitated martyrs and were signs attached to church hostelries, but it has become a satirical allusion to the fact that men, the main frequenters of pubs in the past mistakenly believe that women talk more than they do

ROB ROY

8.5" high. Rd. No. 607261. 1912. On the reverse AC 1912, and on the base GREENLEES BROTHERS CLAYMORE SCOTCH WHISKY DISTILLERS.

ROB ROY MACGREGOR, 1671-1734, was a dangerous and powerful outlaw who ran a protection racket in the Highlands of Scotland but, as he blackmailed the rich landowners, opposed the government agents and was capable of acts of justice and even generosity, he became an accepted popular hero, and appears in a novel bearing his name by Sir Walter Scott.

A SAILOR'S STORY

8.5" flask with an angular handle and silver stopper.

A group of sailors gathered around a tavern table drinking and smoking. One of them is telling a yarn to which the others are listening avidly. A ships model is suspended from the ceiling, not an English custom but common practice on the continent. Similar subjects were often hand painted on Burslem vases in the style of the Dutch "Old Masters". See page 37

"SPORTING SQUIRE"

Rd. No. 578705. 1909. Found in three variations. Tall pear shaped flask, 8" high, with or without title, and on the reverse, DEWAR'S WHISKY. Small globular flask, 6" high, with DEWAR'S in large type on the reverse. Medium globular flask, 6.5" high, with DEWAR'S on the reverse, and at the side a printed commemorative medallion with the Royal cipher and G & M 1911. Issued to commemorate the Coronation of George V and Queen Mary.

See also "Huntsman Fox".

THE SQUIRE of some standing in country society, was expected to take part in the important country pursuit of fox hunting. Here he is shown in hunting 'pink', black hunting hat and with a horseshoe cravat pin. Normally a good luck talisman, the horseshoe is here reversed, superstitiously thought to be unlucky as 'the luck will run out'.

A STATE GOVERNOR A 100 years ago.

7" flask. Full title appears on the face. On the reverse AC 1911 and printed on the base, GREENLEES BROTHERS CLAYMORE SCOTCH WHISKY.

THE STATE GOVERNOR in the United States is a powerful figure granted wide powers by the constitution, in the internal affairs of his state. Here is an early nineteenth century interior with a family portrait on the wall and the Governor at ease in his home with a flask of wine and a glass by his side. There are two Greenlees flasks for 1911. Perhaps this was produced for export to the United States only.

"STIGGINS"
from *Pickwick Papers* by Charles Dickens

8" high. Issued in 1936. Titled and showing an interior with decanters of wine prominently displayed.

THE REVEREND MISTER STIGGINS, a drunken hypocrite and leading light at the Brick Lane Temperence meetings until exposed by Tony Weller. *He was a prim-faced, red nosed man, with a long, thin countenance, and a semi-rattlesnake sort of eye rather sharp, but decidedly bad.*

TAM O'SHANTER pursued by the witches.

7" flask. Rd. No. 589109-1911. Full title on the face. On the reverse AC 1911. Printed on the base is GREENLEES BROTHERS CLAYMORE SCOTCH WHISKY DISTILLERS.

TAM O'SHANTER - a poem by Robert Burns (1790) tells of a farmer returning home one night well primed with liquor, coming upon the devil with attendant witches. He is chased by a witch and attempts to cross the Bridge of Doon, where he will be out of her power. He reaches safety but his grey mare loses her tail to the witch as they fly across the Bridge, the scene on the flask.

TAVERN SCENES

6.5" high. Globular flask. Depicts a sixteenth century Elizabethan tavern scene showing the landlord and the serving maid with two customers dressed as seamen of the time. On the reverse is a seated figure and a barrel.

We have already mentioned other tavern scenes depicted on Kingsware flasks: *Dr Johnson, A Sailor's Story, A Fish Story, The Leather Bottle* and there are others shown on the Spirit Barrels. The rarer barrel is the upright form. Both have pottery stands but the horizontal barrel, 7" long, can also have a wooden version. Both have fittings marked G.B. Betjemann. Dated 1928+. They could be supplied with six barrel shaped tots with silver bases. Both barrels show Elizabethan scenes of the landlord serving his customers, serving wenches and customers drinking.

Burslem handpainted vase with Tavern Scene

TONY WELLER Beware of the Vidders

from *Pickwick Papers* by Charles Dickens.

8" high. DEWARS ON THE BASE. Incised *Noke*. (The 'V' being a Doulton innovation). A non DEWARS version exists with silver stopper and chain. A version exists with *DEWAR'S Imperial* on the reverse.

TONY WELLER also occurs as a figural flask. 10" high. He has a hole in his hat to take the cork and a hole in the hand to take a wooden and twine whip which is usually missing. Incised on the body is *Tony Weller* and *Noke*. Silver Hallmarks 1911 and 1925.

TONY WELLER, a stage-coachman and a widower, marries again an uncommon pleasant widder, but lives to regret his imprudence and warns others, *"Beware of the widders"*. His second wife obligingly dies and leaves him to enjoy his single state, having inherited her pub, *The Marquis of Granby*.

UNCLE SAM

7.5" high. Rd. No. 504944. 1907. DEWAR'S SCOTCH WHISKY on the reverse. D99.

'UNCLE SAM' is a jocular name for the government (or people) of the United States, a facetious interpretation of the initials U.S. He is personified in his traditional dress of stars and stripes and is acceptably smoking the North American product, tobacco, whereas the imbibing of alcohol might be frowned upon in so worthy a fellow.

"NIGHT WATCHMAN"

Two different shapes, different colourings and many variations of lettering occur. Tall cylindrical flask 10.5" high, with DEWAR'S WHISKY on the reverse.

Yet another has the motto *Here's to thee, my honest friend, Wishing these hard times many mend.* A flattened globular shape, 7.25" high, with title on the face and DEWAR'S on the base. Rd. No. 400172, 1902, makes it one of the earliest designs issued in Kingsware. It is based on similar designs issued on other non-Kingsware objects in 1901.

THE WATCHMAN was the precursor of the policeman. He patrolled the streets of the city at night carrying a lantern and staff, calling the state of the weather and the hour. The watchman was replaced by the 'Peeler', the forerunner of the modern policeman in 1829.

THE WATCHMAN WITH MODELLED HEAD occurs in two versions, a tall one 10" high, and a globular one 8" high, both with modelled head at the neck, but with various transfers of the watchman on the body - all used on Noke's *Night Watchman* seriesware. With a silver stopper and chain marked G.B. & Sons Rd. Nos. 436947 and 436948 (the taller). 1904. One of each of these two shapes occur as miniatures, 3.75" and 4.25", in exact replica and with the same registered numbers, but very often the transfers are missing. The globular version of the watchman with modelled head occurs with an added transfer on the body for *Clan MacKenzie Scotch Whisky*, a stags head, and the Gaelic, *Cuidich and Rich* - Help the King, being the motto of the Clan MacKenzie..

"Green" versions also exist.

WIZARD

Tall cylindrical flask, 10" high. Rd. No. 435657. 1904. Silver stopper and chain. Incised *Noke*.

THE WIZARD or sorcerer, clad in a long robe covered with strange symbols and wearing the broad brimmed, pointed hat of his trade, works into the night chanting spells over his cauldron of magic potion, accompanied only by the nocturnal bat.

Throughout the list, if the title appears on the flask it is printed in inverted commas, if not, I have had to assign what I hope is an appropriate title. Lack of printed titles has always led to difficulties.

"GREEN VERSIONS"

These are made in the usual moulds with an ivory base. They are glazed with greens and yellows rather than shades of brown. The flasks with modelled heads seem often to appear in this finish.

Green versions of *Bill Sikes*, *The Pied Piper* & *The Watchman*.

QUEENSWARE is the true partner to Kingsware. The production methods are exactly the same. Only the body is different being in the usual ivory coloured clay instead of the terracotta used for *Kingsware*. The subjects are decorated in the same pale well bonded colours fused with the body but unfortunately, in my opinion, the whole effect is rather muddy and unattractive. Others must have thought so at the same time as it was not popular and was made in small quantities compared with Kingsware. Consequently, as with all rarities, it is very sought after today, especially in Australia where much of it was exported. Because of the varying shrinkage factors of the two different clay bodies, *Queensware* pieces tend sometimes to be slightly larger than their *Kingsware* equivalents. The first mention of *Queensware* in the Doulton pattern books is in 1932 but it was probably in production before that date. In fact we have a *Hogarth* jug D5173 for 1931.

ADVERTISING FLASKS in this medium were made for *H & A Dickens Whisky*. *Mr Pickwick from Dickens*, 1939, *Mr Micawber* and *Tony Weller* certainly were. Whether the *Queensware* Dickens subjects *Stiggins* and *Mr Pickwick Proposes a Toast* were also made for this firm I don't know because, of course, the paper labels have often been washed off through the years. There is a very strange looking *Uncle Sam* flask with bands of colour sometimes with A C 1907 on the reverse and *Dewars White Label Whisky* on the base. Other flasks found are:- *The Alchemist, John Barleycorn, Fisherman, Memories, The Monk, Pied Piper*, and there are others. *The Mr Pickwick from Dickens flask* was made exclusively in *Queensware*, is 8.5" high and shows Mr Pickwick in close-up with two other Pickwickians, and a banner beneath.

Mr Pickwick from Dickens, Mr Micawber for *H & A Dickens Whisky* and *Pied Piper* and *Uncle Sam* in *Queensware*.

The *Alchemist, Memories, Micawber & Fisherman* flasks, *Hogarth* Jug. *The Billings Collection*

Tony Weller, Stiggins, Mr Pickwick proposes flasks in Queensware.

The *Monk* flask & *Parson Brown* jug in both Kingsware and Queensware and *Charles Dickens* jug

QUEENSWARE JUGS include:-

Hogarth with Pipe	6.5"	D5173	1931
Smoker Tankard	4.5"	D5598	1935
Tavern Scene - Bowls	6.5"	D5705	1936
The Dickens Jug	7.5"	D5708	1936
Golfers	9"	D5716	1936
Queen Elizabeth I	6.5"	D5717	1936
Parson Brown	7"	D5718	1936

Of these only the *Queen Elizabeth I* jug has not yet been found in Kingsware and in fact this is a most successful design in Queensware.

TABLEWARES occur in Queensware and there seems to be a complete range for *Dame* and *The Cup That Cheers* complete with tea caddy and plates. *Don Quixote* pieces exist too and although I have not seen other designs yet I feel more were made.

D5598 Smoker Tankard 4.5" 1935.

Don Quixote Tableware

EMBOSSED SUBJECTS found as Kingsware and Queensware exist in yet a further finish which is known as 'Aerographed Brown'. This uses a normal ivory earthenware base. The colours are added to the shape after it has left the mould, in the usual under glaze painted manner. The colours lack the soft effect of the previous methods being much sharper and more vibrant with definite reds, greens and browns etc. These wares are given further distinguishing feature by having handles, necks and bases Aerographed with a spray painting technique. This can be a dark brown colour known as *Drake* Brown (as used on the *Drake* jug) or a lighter shade called *John Barleycorn* brown. The tankard with the smoker in the broad brimmed hat is airbrushed in green. This airbrushing technique is the same as that used on the early character jugs 1935 - 1940, with production being interrupted by the war and not revived after. A table of the titles found decorated in the various methods with spaces you can fill in as more are found is on page 72.

Queen Elizabeth Jug 6.5" 1936
Dickens Jug 7"
Memories flask 9.5"
Smoker Tankard D.5598 1935
Airbrushed in green

KINGSWARE JUGS

Jugs are found in the following designs and there must be others.

CAVALIER 5.5" with pipe

DICKENS 7" D2847 1907 Incised *Noke*
Charles Dickens head forms the spout. Characters around the body are; Sydney Carton, Fagin, Bill Sikes, Sam Weller, Pickwick, Pecksniff.

DON QUIXOTE 8.75" and beakers 4". D4965. 1929

DRAKE 9" and tankards 5.5" 1938   DUKE OF YORK 7.5" 1940

FOX HUNTING Tall 11" bulbows 8" and tankards 4" D2769 1905

GEORGE V 7" 1911   GOLFING 9" D4973 1930

"HAPPY DAYS" Smoker with church warden, "Reverie" ladies in smoke. Title on reverse.

HOGARTH - series of jugs in five main sizes 4" - 9" D1363 1902. Shape is "Bardolf".

Sometimes with pipe, sometimes tankard, sometimes holding jug of ale, with art nouveau decorations.

IN THE STOCKS 7" jester in the stocks D4966 1929

LEATHER BLACKJACK simulated leather jug, 7" 1929

MEMORIES Dickens and his characters 6.5" D2693 1906

MEMORIES 17thC man with cavaliers, a monk and jester 6.5"

MEMORIES 18thC man with wigged gentlemen 6.5"

MENDOZA 5"

PARSON BROWN Various sizes } with title and without.

PARSON JONES

MR PICKWICK & SAM WELLER 6.5"

MR PICKWICK PROPOSES 4.5". "The Pickwickians"

QUINCE Smoker with scull cap

"VIRGINIA" Smoker in broad brimmed hat, 5"
D1618 1903 D2136 1904

WARATAH 5"

WATCHMAN 7.5" and 6" and others with various mottos 1902

WIZARD ewer 11" and 16"

A jug without a spout becomes a tankard. A beaker has no handle. *Golfers* appears as a tankard and a beaker. Both of them come in sets of six to complement the jugs and make a beer set. I have seen the *Fox hunting* set also as a jug and six tankards, and *Drake* and other designs were probably sold this way.

TANKARDS exist in the following designs:

DRAKE 6"

FOX HUNTING 4"

GOLFERS 6" Tankard, 4" Beaker

VIRGINIA 4"

Smoker Skull cap 5.5"

HOGARTH 4"

MINSTRELS Lute & Violin 4"

DON QUIXOTE 4" Beaker

WATCHMAN

GEORGE V CORONATION 1911 5"

48

TOBY JUGS

There are two Kingsware tobies: The Huntsman 7" D6320 1950 and The Squire 6" D6319 1950. These models are very similar to the two models by Harry Fenton, introduced into the general range in 1950, and were probably his designs too. The Squire has a ridged top to take a silver rim as many pieces had. The silver looks very good against the dark Kingsware body. Very often rims are missing. Doulton would not have fitted them, so perhaps some were never done and yet others have had the silver removed for scrap in the past when the silver was more valuable than the Kingsware. The position is reversed today and the addition of a silver rim does not add much to the value.

KINGSWARE ADVERTISING JUGS

PETER DAWSON LIMITED, 82 Great Clyde Street, Glasgow, Scotland.

Jug (103) 4" *Peter Dawson's Scotch* with yellow harebells 1907.

Jug (104) 5" *Peter Dawson;s Scotch* with yellow harebells 1907.

The Harebell is "the Bluebell of Scotland".

D & J MC CALLUM, Distillers, Edinburgh, Scotland.

McCALLUM CHARACTER JUG (269) 6.5" 1,000 - 1,500 made c 1930. Similar jugs to the *McCallum* and *Dawson* jugs were made by other suppliers, suggesting the designs were the advertisers copyright. However, the Doulton Kingsware versions are superior to those of other makers.

Fireside Vase 3.25"

Pied Piper vase 12", *Wizard Vase* 12", *Witch Urn* 13", all incised *Noke* shown with *The Crown Peace* and *Bill Sikes* flasks. Large Pipe tobacco jar made for George Betjemann 1909.
Tavern Scene spirit barrel and the large 12" *pipe* shaped tobacco jar with silver mount marked *G.B. &*
Sons Rd No. 547962 1909.   *Courtesy Phillips*

KINGSWARE VASES

The Doulton design books show numerous shapes and designs for Kingsware vases and Loving Cups, so I feel the combinations of shape and character must be innumerable and probably all I can list are some of the subjects found.

Cavalier, Fox Hunting, Fireside, Jester, Dr Johnson, Minstrels, Monk in Cellar, Mr Pickwick, Pied Piper, A Sailor's Story, Tavern Scenes, exterior and interiors including a game of bowls, *(Lynton) Witch, Wizard.* Most of these subjects appear in many different poses. Vases were advertised in sizes from 3" to 12" for prices between 2/8 and 14/- (70 pence) in 1932. Note there are at least three versions of a *Witch* and at least five different *Tavern Scenes.* See end papers for the many other shapes.

Tavern Vase 6"

Tavern vase showing a game of bowls 6"

Vase with a *Jester* 4" and an Elizabethan character, very much as *Bardolf* would be portrayed. *Bill Sikes* miniature and a *Hogarth* tankard.

51

LOVING CUPS

HUNTSMAN 7" D2769 1907 Hounds on reverse.

HERE'S A HEALTH UNTO HIS MAJESTY 13" D5719 1936.

DR JOHNSON TAVERN SCENE WITH PUNCH BOWL 13".

CAVALIER 5"

FISHERMAN 5"

Here's a Health Unto His Majesty Loving Cup sold for 19s 6d (85 pence) in 1932. The design was adapted for a flask in 1936.

MINIATURES - FLASKS

There are five miniature flasks with a capacity so small that they fall more into the novelty bracket than being of any practical use. They have neat silver fittings and were probably meant as amusing gifts for "the man who has everything". *Bill Sikes* silver hallmark bears a makers name of *G. B. & Sons* for *George Betjemann & Sons*. Their silver marks range from 1905 - 1909. Three of them are quite readily found and I am doubtful that the statement "only 200 were made" is true of the *Tony Weller* flask as so many survive. The fact that *Bill Sikes* is so rarely found when the two *Watchman* versions were obviously made in quantity is surprising. Many of the *Watchman* miniatures are found without their transfers. Whether these were "seconds" doesn't really matter as all are now desirable. *Tony Weller* has a great variation in colouring with red to brown waistcoat and even black or white buttons, which excites some collectors.

WATCHMAN with modelled head tall 3.75" watchman transfer.

WATCHMAN with modelled head globular 3.5" D1853 1903 watchman transfer.

BILL SIKES with modelled head 3.5" *Bullseye* transfer 1905.

COACHMAN figural with his head for a stopper, 5.5" D2944 1908.

TONY WELLER figural 3.5".

MINIATURES - JUGS, VASES AND LOVING CUPS All around 2" high.

There seem to be a set of six Dickens characters represented on these miniatures. They were all meant to have silver rims originally. On their reverse is an embossed shield shape with the title, i.e. *Dickens Sam Weller, Dickens Weller Senior*.

MR PICKWICK Jug

PECKSNIFF Vase

FAGIN Jug

TONY WELLER Vase and Loving Cup

SAM WELLER Vase and Loving Cup

BILL SIKES Loving Cup

The characters can occur on different shapes.

CLOCKS

Five characters have been found as clocks which come in three shapes. They have elaborate *art nouveau* decorations fashionable at the time.

1. ALCHEMIST 8.5" 435890 1904
2. JESTER 6"
4. MONK 12"
5. NIGHT WATCHMAN 12"
3. PIED PIPER 12"

CANDLESTICKS

FOX HUNTING 10" D2769 1907+

SHAVING MUGS

FRIAR 4" with barber's bowl

MEPHISTO

LIDDED BOX D2693 MEMORIES - Dickens characters

CABUCHONS These are found mounted as hat pins, cork tops and brooches. 1.5" diameter

ELIZABETHAN MAN WITH RUFF   FLEMISH LADY WITH KERCHIEF

MAN IN TRICORN HAT   LADY WITH GREEN SCARF

LADY WITH DOLLY VARDON HAT

The silver mounts have been found dated 1907 and 1909.

There must be other objects and characters to find.

SMOKING ACCESSORIES

KINGSWARE was assumed to be a particularly male taste, consequently Doulton made many "Smoking Requisites" in this finish. They were sold in high class tobacconists and general stores. The 12" novelty pipe with the bowl serving as a tobacco jar is embossed on the base as being exclusively supplied by George Betjemann & Sons. In a shape book in the Doulton archives, pages 139 and 140 are labelled "Betjemann's Specialities", suggesting many designs were supplied to this firm. The silver cork from the *Bill Sikes* miniature is marked "G B & Sons" and the horizontal barrel to name but two pieces.

Smoker in Skullcap on *Virginia* tobacco jar with airbrushed brown tankard in the same design.

TOBACCO JARS are found in the following form:-

Single modelled fox on lid of oval bowl

Two curled foxes on lid of oval bowl 1937.

Hound modelled as a lid on a round bowl.

Character Dogs from HN range in regular glaze attached to lid of round bowl.

The above bowls were decorated with running foxes, hounds and rats as appropriate.

Mephisto matchstand

Mr Pickwick Proposes Tobacco Jar

TOBACCO JARS

Monks 6" Virginia jar D1070 1901.

Fox Hunting 5'5" globular jar D2769 1907.

Mr Pickwick and Sam Weller D4350 1923.

Mr Pickwick Proposes a Toast 5.5" globular jar.

Golfers 6.5" large globular jar D4973 1930.

Smoker in Skull Cap and Pipe 5" "Virginia" jar 1904.

Smoker in Broad Brimmed Hat "Virginia" D2136 1904.

Smoker in Smoking Cap and Pipe with two handles.

Parson Brown 6" "Virginia" jar.

Fisherman 6"

Forty Thieves 6" jar. Noke.

Fireside D4351 1923.

Spaniel's Head in relief on large globular jar 7"

OTHER SMOKING ACCESSORIES

Alchemist - Cigar holder 3.5". Striker 3". Ashtray 5.5".

Fireside - Matchstand. D4351 1923.

Fisherman - Matchstriker and ashtray.

Forty Thieves - Ashtray *One of the Forty* 5" c1930

Four Heads - Ashtray, different mottos. D1286 1902.

George V Coronation 3" Matchball. 1911.

Golfers - Matchball. *Ye 19th Hole* ashtray. 04973 1930.

Mephisto - Matchstand, and pipe & ashtray c1902.

Mr Pickwick Proposes a Toast - Matchball & ashtray 5".

Parson Brown Tobacco Jar

Golfers, man in smoking cap, & *Fox hunting* tobacco jars with *Fox hunting* tankard.
One of the Forty ashtray; Four heads ashtray 1902; *George V* matchball 1911.

ABLEWARE is another area where many Kingsware pieces are found. I can't help feeling it was ore suited for display rather than use. The body being so soft and the glaze being prone to crazing doesn't make a suitable container for hot liquids and won't take a lot of "washing up". It will be und that many teapots in particular have been badly damaged over the years unless they have never ft the china cabinet.

he *Darby and Joan,* and *Dame* designs decorated sets of teaware. You will see from the photographs at the *Dame* can appear in various poses and even different hats. Also it can be either plain or tube ned with *Hearts Content* or *The Cup That Cheers* and with or without silver mounts. The design number r the vignettes is D1099 issued in 1901 making this teaware one of the earliest Kingsware designs. oulton named one of their teapot shapes "Joan".

Two Kingsware tea plates and the *Forty Thieves* tobacco jar, 6".

Here are some recorded tableware patterns:

D1099   *Dame* teapot sugar 4", cream 3", cups, saucers and plates. 1901 teapot in 3 sizes

D2695   *Dame* teacaddy 5", teapot stand. 1906

D2870   *Darby and Joan* Royles teapot 8", sugar and cream. 1907

D1286   *Lynton Witch* teapot, sugar and cream. Rectangular shape. 1902

D1286   *Wizard* teapot, sugar and cream. 1902

D2769   *Fox Hunting,* tea and coffe sets. 1907

D2940   *Pied Piper,* tea and coffee sets, teapot 6", coffee jug 7.5". 1908

D4351   *Fireside,* teapot, sugar and milk. "At eventide". 1923. Teapot in 3 sizes.

D4965   *Don Quixote and Sancho Panza,* teasets.

         Dr Johnson, teasets. 1929

D5068   Dickens characters, teapots: *Mr and Mrs Micawber, Sairey Gamp, Mr Pickwick* and *Sam Weller.* 1930

         Biscuit Barrel Fox-hunting 6"

         Condiment set of three pieces, Hogarth salt 2.5".

D4350   Dickens Coffee pots, *Mr Pickwick and Sam Weller, Sam Weller* 7", *Tony Weller* 6.25". Also coffee and tea ware.

The ROYLES PATENT SELF POURING TEAPOT is the most spectacular version. The invention dates from 1890 and Doulton manufactured it in many finishes. It works on a hydraulic principle and pours tea when the lid is lifted so that it is not necessary to lift the pot. It shows *Darby and Joan* on the front and this title in a ribboned shield on the reverse.

It is 8" high and its design number 2870 tells us it was first issued in 1907.

The *Pied Piper* design was one of the most popular choices for tablewares.   There are silver mounted tea and coffee sets and even a 'green' version. Teapot 5" high 1905.   The *Fox Hunting* tableware has rusticated handles, Coffee pot 7"

61

OTHER BURSLEM FLASKS AND TWO FROM LAMBETH

These flasks often find themselves in collections alongside Kingsware flasks. However, this section i included mainly to explain titles which were sometimes erroneously thought to be Kingsware becaus they were included in a much published memo sent to Shorters of Sydney, Australia, by an E.M.C. a Doultons on 2nd February 1956. In his very useful sale catalogue of *Early Historic and Rare Bottles* date 26th September 1979, David Westcott published the list under the title *Royal Doulton Kingsware* whic added to the confusion.

The memo to Shorters set out a list of various flasks purporting to be 'fine earthenware flagons whic were supplied to John Dewar and Sons Ltd by Doulton'. Red herrings abounded, some had wron titles, many were not Dewar's, one was Lambeth stoneware and in the 1931 list of Kingsware subject listed as having been supplied to Dewar's, not one was! However, at the time it was the only lis available. I explain a few of the titles included to show how knowledge of the subject has advance in the last thirteen years and hoping that a future researcher will make the complete translation an eliminate *Hogarth*, which has still not been found on a flask nor *Ye Weary Pilgrim* positively identifie

SYDNEY HARBOUR
NO. 156.

Triangular flask. 6.5" high x 7" wide. DEWAR'S on the reverse. Rd No. 636615. 1914. with black border and transfer with yellow and orange. This last printing is sometimes missing, signifying a "second".

The scene commemorates a flight over Sydney Harbour by Maurice Guillaux in his Bleriot Monoplan XI in 1914. The subject of this flask has always been a puzzle until now, for Doulton sometimes referre to it loosely as "Louis Bleriot". Perhaps we may be forgiven for expanding on our information. LOUI BLERIOT 1872-1936 was an early French aviator and aircraft designer. He was the first man to fly th English Channel in 1909, making an early morning flight of half an hour on July 25th 1909, and winnin the Daily Mail prize of one thousand pounds. It was apparently an effortless success, but flying wa a hazardous occupation at the time. In 1910 30 pilots were killed in crashes despite the fact that man pilots, including Bleriot, had been know to walk out of a crash uninjured. Bleriots wife persuaded hir to confine himself to designing. A Bleriot Monoplane was used on the first air mail flight of six mil in the United States of America in 1911.

A Bleriot was used by the first woman to fly the English Channel in 1912, Harriet Quimby, a American. One would assume Maurice Guillaux shipped his planes out to Australia, as the first fligh from Europe to Australia didn't take place until 1919. M. Guillaux flight tested the first seaplane ove Sydney Harbour on May 8th 1914. That was a Maurice Farman Hydro- Aeroplane and the flask show a Bleriot XI Monoplane. In July 1914 he flew Australia's first airmail run from Melbourne to Sydne with 2,500 items. we haven't got an exact date for the flight on the flask, sometime in May 1914 w can assume, making this a commemorative flask. Elizabeth Nevell of Sydney has been able to furnis us with these facts: The ship and Harbour part of the photograph is similar to that used on Doulto Seriesware, originally reproduced on stationary in use on Royal Mail Lines steamers, so perhaps a original photograph of the event was not used?

MONARCH OF THE GLEN

7.5" high, a transfer printed flask with a green border issued pre 1919 and a *Vandyke* brown border in 1929 with an antler handle. DEWAR'S WHISKY on the reverse.

The Monarch of the Glen was painted by Queen Victoria's favourite artist, Sir Edward Landseer. 1802 -73. It was painted for the refreshment room of the House of Lords and exhibited at the Royal Academy in 1851. However, Parliament refused to vote the necessary purchase money and the painting was bought by Sir Thomas Dewar for 5,000 guineas. It is now at the United Distillers offices in Edinburgh. The Stag is still found and hunted in its wild state in Scotland.

PEACE FLAGON No. 181. 1919.

7.5" high. Rd. No. 670019. 1919. Transfer printed flask with either green 1919 or brown 1929 border. DEWAR or DEWAR's WHISKY on the reverse. The handle is in the form of a dolphin.

A commemorative flagon, depicting Britannia, produced to celebrate the Peace after the First World War.

Britannia, the Latin name of Britain and a poetic name for Britain personified, first appeared on a copper coin of 1672. Frances Stuart, Duchess of Richmond, is said to have been the model.

THE SPIRIT OF FRIENDSHIP

A 9.5" Dewars printed flask with added enamels D78 - 1905. A green glazed top and base. Title around the base. Three national figures around the body, Auld Mac, John Bull and Uncle Sam in drinking attitudes. Printed on the base, a roundel with Dewar's White Label Whisky which designated Dewar's Export Blend.

THE SPIRIT OF OUR ANCESTORS

Three spirit flasks, 7" x 5", formed as simulated leather bound books supplied on a wooden stand. On the spines the titles and volumes 1 - 111 printed in black. Base mark is Royal Doulton England. Probably sold as a set of decanters in high class stores.

SMA' SCOTCH

A 9.5" printed flask with added enamels. D85 - 1905. Green glazed top and base. Printed with white label roundels and Rd. No. 471182 on base. A play on another term for a Wee Dram, the title is printed on the shoulder and the illustration shows some small Scottish Waifs. A spire stopper is shown in the Doulton Design book. The D No's are from this book.

LAMBETH FLASKS

HAYMARKET

A 9" Dewars bottle flask with moulded relief 1908 +. Titled Dewar's Whisky with an overall green glaze. A moulded relief of Dewar House, the firm's London office, in the Haymarket, off Piccadilly Circus, London. The building was designed for Sir Thomas Dewar by F M Elgood ARIBA, in the Scottish Baronial style and opened in 1908. From its earliest days 'the rendevous for every sort of celebrity from cabinet minister to matinee idol'. Its hospitality continued until it closed in 1987.

INDIAN HEAD

A 7" brown glazed double handled flask with an American Indian head applied in white and the blend A C 1908. The base is impressed *Greenlees Brothers Claymore Scotch Whisky Distillers* BB4. Made at Lambeth in 1908, this flask pre-dates the Kingsware range for Greenlees which began in 1909.

65

Pattern book painting showing airbrushed brown versions of *Tony Weller* D5706 and *Memories* flasks D5707 1936.

Courtesy Royal Doulton

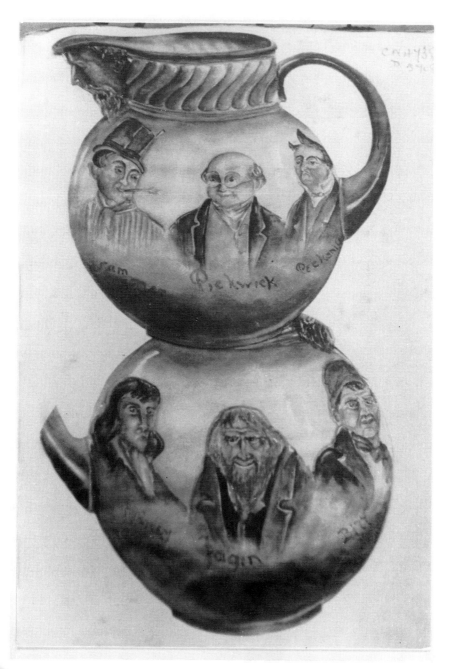

Pattern book painting showing both faces of the *Dickens* jug, airbrushed brown version D5705 1936.

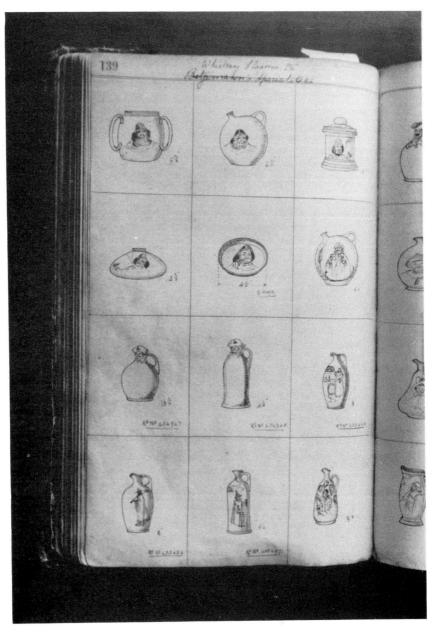

Page 139 in a Doulton design book entitled whisky flagons etc. and *Betjamann's specialities* (crossed through) a *Fisherman* loving cup, flask, tobacco jar, matchstriker and ashtray are shown, two miniature *Watchman* flasks and five others, *John Barleycorn*, *The Monk*, *The Pied Piper*, *Wizard*, and *Memories* all non promotional.

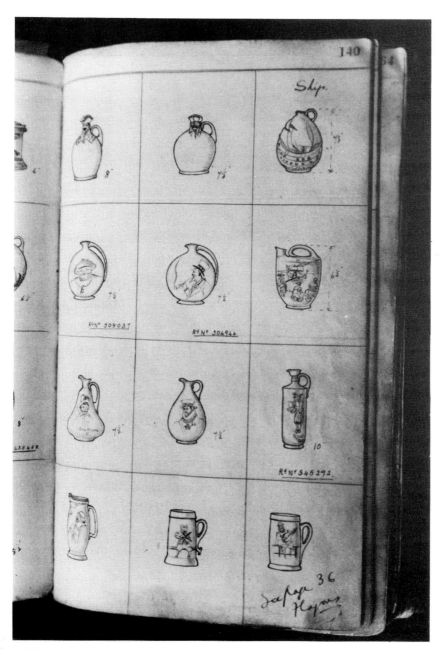

age 140 in the design book. showing nine flasks, a *Bardolf* jug, and two tankards with *Minstrells*, the rst three flasks are non-promotional, *The Galleon* is referred to as *Ship*, five *Dewars* and one *Greenlees* asks are shown. A note says "see page 36 Flagons" but I've not traced that yet.

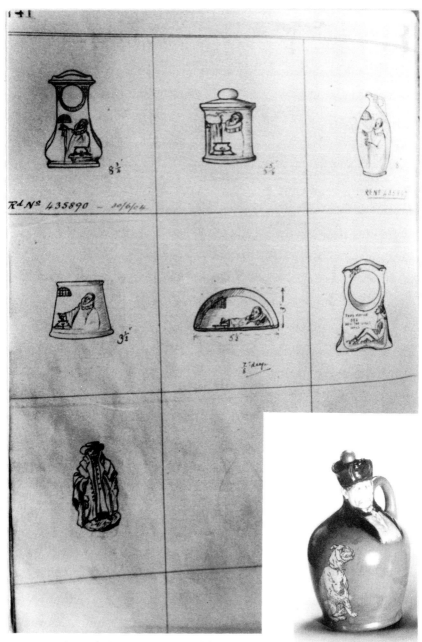

Page 141 in the design book, showing the *Alchemist*
clock, tobacco jar, flask, cigar holder and ashtray,
the *Jester* clock and miniature *Tony Weller* flask.

Bill Sikes flask showing trnsfer of *Bullseye*.

MOTTOS are often tube lined on pieces of Kingsware. Sometimes they express a particularly apt sentiment, such as *The Cup that Cheers* on teaware and references to tobacco on smoking accessories. The same motto occurs on varying shapes and vice versa. They are amusing variations to collect as a specialist section in Kingsware.

Here are some of the sayings found:-

"A BUMPER TO HER WHO ADORES ME AND ANOTHER TO HER I ADORE" (Loving Cup)

"BE CONTENT THE SEA HAS FISH ENOUGH" (four faces ashtray)

"THE CUP THAT CHEERS" (teawares)

"DRINK WISELY" (tankards and jugs)

"ENOUGH'S AS GOOD AS A FEAST" (Watchman jug)

"FOR THY SAKE TOBACCO I WOULD DO ANYTHING BUT DIE" (four faces ashtray)

"HAPPY DAYS" (jug)

"HEARTS CONTENT" (teaware)

"HERE'S A HEALTH UNTO HIS MAJESTY" (flask and loving cup)

"HERE'S TO THEE, MY HONEST FRIEND, WISHING THESE HARD TIMES MAY MEND (Watchman flask)

"HERE'S TO THE MAN WHO IS PLEASED WITH HIS LOT, WHO NEVER SITS SIGHING FOR WHAT HE HAS NOT: CONTENTED AND THANKFUL, FOR WHAT HE HAS GOT" (punch bowl and loving cup)

"IT'S HARD FOR AN EMPTY BAG TO STAND UPRIGHT:" (jug)

"ONE'S OWN OPINION IS NEVER WRONG" (jug)

"QUARRELLING DOGS COME HALTING HOME" (Watchman jug)

"THOUGH OTHERS PURSES BE MORE FAT, WHY SHOULD WE PINE OR GRIEVE FOR THAT, HANG SORROW, CARE WILL KILL A CAT AND THEREFORE LET'S BE MERRY" (jug)

"THUS MAY WE SEE HOW THE WORLD WAGS" (Clock)

"WHEN THIS YOU SEE REMEMBER ME, THOUGH MANY MILES WE DISTANT BE" (Loving Cup)

"WOULD YOU KNOW THE VALUE OF MONEY, TRY TO BORROW SOME" (jug)

"VESSELS LARGE MAY VENTURE MORE BUT LITTLE BOATS KEEP NEAR THE SHORE" (jug)

FLASKS	KINGSWARE	QUEENSWARE	AIRBRUSHED BROWN
Alchemist	•	•	
John Barleycorn	•	• D5596	
Fisherman	•	•	
Memories	•	•	• D5707
Monk	•	•	
Mr Micawber	•	•	•
Mr Pickwick	•		• D5721
Mr Pickwick from Dickens		•	
Mr Pickwick Proposes	•	• D5720	• D5722
Pied Piper	•	•	•
Stiggins	•	•	
Tony Weller	•	•	•D5706
Uncle Sam	•	•	•
JUGS			
Dickens	• D2847	•	• D5708
Drake	•		• D5705
Golfers	•	•	• D5716
Hogarth with Pipe	• D2940	• D5173	
Hogarth with Tankard	• D1363		• D5596
Parson Brown	•	•	• D5718
Queen Elizabeth I		•	• D5717
TANKARDS			
Drake	•		• D5705
Golfers	•		• D5716
Fox Hunting	•		• D5595
Smoker in Skullcap	•		• D5597
Virginia	• D2136	•	• D5598 Gree
MISCELLANEOUS			
Don Quixote/Sancho Panza sugar and cream set	•	• D4965	
Dutch Children	• D1071		• D5720
Here's a Health unto His Majesty vase	•		• D5719
Dame Teapot	•D1099	•	• D5704

ADDITIONAL CHARACTERS NOT FOUND ON KINGSWARE FLASKS

DARBY & JOAN are the epitome of a devoted old married couple. They were first named in a poem in the Gentleman's Magazine of 1735.

DRAKE, Sir Francis Drake, c1545-1596, circum-navigator and an Admiral of the British Fleet, is shown with a companion bowling on Plymouth Hoe whilst spectators look on. On the reverse a fire beacon is being lighted to warn of the approach of the Spanish Armada which is seen in the background sailing up the English Channel. According to legend, Drake finished his game in a leisurely fashion and then set off to defeat the superior Spanish fleet utterly. The leisurely start was, in fact, due to the practical reason of waiting for the title.

DUKE OF YORK, Frederick Augustus, 1763-1827, second son of George III and Commander in Chief of the British army 1798-1809. A military incompetent, the nursery rhyme about the Grand Old Duke of York commemorates this. Doulton's quote on the jug is "the brave old Duke of York", which I don't think he was.

ELIZABETH I, inherited a troubled England in 1668 but her popularity, cleverness and moderate inclinations created a golden age of great statesmen: Howard, Walsingham and the Cecils; great adventurers: Drake, Raleigh and Frobisher and great playwrights: Shakespeare, Marlowe and Jonson. Drake and the captains of Elizabeth I kept the Spaniards at Bay, protestantism was assured, great discoveries were made. At her death in 1603, aged 70, she left England a first class power.

HOGARTH D1363 1902. William Hogarth, 1697-1764, a celebrated engraver and painter who satirised his times, particularly in relation to the pleasure and follies of drinking.
The turban was fashionable male attire at this time and Hogarth is often shown wearing one so I think this a very strong link between the turbaned man design with its many poses, appearing on jugs and this title.

LYNTON WITCH Lynton, Devon is named for the River Lyn (Torrent in old English). The Lyn runs through the steep sided "Valley of the Rocks", a forbidding place of curious rock formations. These limestone regions in England often generate legends as people see likenesses in the strange forms. Lynton is no exception and has its "White Lady". Is she the origin of Doulton's very classic witch with pointed hat, cauldren and cat? I think it more likely she is derived from *Mother Meldrun* who sheltered *under eaves of Lichened rock* when *Jan Ridd*, the hero of *Lorna Doone* came to consult her. Blackmore's novel was very popular in 1902 when this design was introduced. Kingsware has two other witch designs, see page 50.

PARSON BROWN AND PARSON JONES represent two typical merry, drinking clergymen.

VIRGINIA D2136 1904. This name is given to the straightsided tobacco jar that appears in three sizes by Doulton who often named a shape after the first character appearing on it. Such as the Joan teapot. The seventeenth century character with the broad brimmed hat must surely be from Virginia. Founded by Sir Walter Raleigh, who named it for Queen Elizabeth I, the 'Virgin Queen', Virginia in the United States was settled as an English colony in 1584. The settlement was a failure, but the returning colonists led by Ralph Lane, their Governor, in 1586 brought back with them to England the smoking habit they had learned from the Indians. Virginia has ever since been renowned for its fine tobacco.

BARDOLF is also a name given to a shape. He was a character in three of Shakespeare's plays. A friend of Falstaff and one of his disreputable drinking companions. He ended as a tapster at the Garter Inn. He's described as *white livered and red faced*.

QUINCE In a Doulton catalogue a tankard with the smoker in a skull cap is given this name, but again I'm sure this refers to the shape only. *Quince* is another Shakespearean character, a carpenter in *A Midsummer Night's Dream*.

WARATAH. This is the floral emblem of New South Wales, Australia. Its botanic name means *'most beautiful plant seen from afar'*. It is prolific around Sydney.

DATING

Although I have not yet succeeded in positively dating every design, we can place many of them using the various methods of dating available to us.

REGISTERED NUMBERS 1902-1919

385500 . . 1902	494000 . . 1907	594000 . . 1912
402500 . . 1903	519000 . . 1908	625000 . . 1913
420000 . . 1904	530000 . . 1909	642000 . . 1914
447000 . . 1905	550000 . . 1910	660000 . . 1918
471000 . . 1906	588000 . . 1911	670000 . . 1919

Registered numbers appear on the base of many of the pieces.
Here is a list of flasks found with these printed numbers:

Night Watchman	400172	1902
Pied Piper	435656	1904
Wizard	435657	1904
Monk	435658	1904
Alchemist	435887	1904
Watchman Modelled Head Glob:	436947	1904
Tall:	436948	1904
Arkwright	471183	1906
Church Warden	486689	1906
Uncle Sam	504944	1907
Falstaff	508037	1907
Beefeater	527012	1908
Jovial Monk	527013	1908
Ben Johnson	543367	1909
George the Guard	545291	1909
Oyez! Oyez!	545292	1909
Sporting Squire	578705	1910
The State Governor	588110	1911
Tam O'Shanter	589109	1911
Rob Roy	607261	1912
Bonnie Prince Charlie	618840	1912
Crusader	625349	1913
Sydney Harbour	636615	1914
Hooked	641908	1914
Nelson I	649343	1914
Admiral of the Fleet	660262	1918
Peace	670019	1919

The year given denotes when the design was registered so the design could not have been issued before that date, but perhaps for many years after.

DOULTON DESIGN NUMBERS appear in the design books and on old catalogue pages. This method of dating is full of pit falls as the same design was issued again and again and, when re-issued as a different shape or in a different finish like Queensware, could be allocated a completely new number.

Design	Item	Date
1070	*Monk* tobacco jar	1901
1071	*Dutch Children* tobacco jar	1901
1099	*Dame* teapot	1901
1286	*Four Heads* ashtray	1902
1363	*Hogarth* jug	1902
1853	*Night Watchman* and modelled head flasks	1903
2136	Smoker B.B.H. jug	1904
2693	*Memories* jug, Dickens	1906
2695	*Dame* tea caddy	1906
2769	*Huntsman* loving cup	1907
2847	*Dickens* jug	1907
2870	*Darby and Joan* teapot	1907
2940	*Hogarth* jug	1908
2944	*Coachman* mini flask	1908
4350	*Mr Pickwick* tobacco jar	1923
4351	*Fireside* tobacco jar	1923
4965	*Don Quixote* jug and flask	1929
4966	*In the Stocks* jug	1929
4973	*Golfers* match ball	1930
5068	*Dickens* character teaset	1930
5173	*Hogarth* jug Queensware	1931
5595	*Fox Hunting*	1935
5596	*Hogarth* jug A. Brown	1935
5597	Skullcap with pipe and mug A. B.	1935
5598	*Smoker B.B.H.* and pipe jug A. Green	1935
5704	*Dame* teapot A. B.	1935
5705	*Drake* jug and mug A. B.	1936
5706	*Tony Weller* flask A. B.	1936
5707	*Memories* flask A. B.	1936
5708	*Dickens* jug A. B.	1936
5716	*Golfers* mug and jug A. B.	1936
5717	*Queen Elizbeth I* jug A. B.	1936
5718	*Parson Brown* jug A. B.	1936
5719	*Here's a Health Unto His Majesty* loving cup A. B.	1937
5720	*Dutch Children* bowl A. B.	1937
5721	*Mr Pickwick* flask A. B.	1937
5722	*Mr Pickwick Proposes a Toast* A. B.	1937

SILVER HALLMARKS

Many Kingsware pieces are silver mounted as the metal looks so good against the dark body. This is a good way of dating tobacco jars and tableware but when it comes to flasks with silver stoppers chains and rings, take into consideration that the stopper could have belonged to another flask at some time. However, spirit barrels and pieces with fixed fittings can definately be dated that way. Many stoppers are dated 1904 and could have been used on later issues.

COMMISSIONED DESIGNS

The 2 and 3 digit numbers in the text refer to the sequence of the Burslem Advertising Design book. This enables us to date one further flask, the Triangular *Nelson D326 - 1935*.

MR PICKWICK FROM DICKENS, the Queensware flask made for *H & A Dickens*. Whisky is found with another form of dating unique to Doulton who introduced this coding system in 1927, when 1 was placed to the right of the backstamp. The flask has 12 which, by adding 27 gives us 1939.

THE GREENLEES FLASKS are dated with a special blend issue A. C. Appellation Contrôlée followed by a date. Purists will realise that there is an advertisers license here but it does give us some definite dates.

Year	Mark	Year	Mark	Year	Mark
1902	g	1916	a	1933	S
1903	h	1917	b	1934	t
1904	i	1918	c	1935	u
1905	k	1919	d		
1906	l	1920	e	Edw. VIII	
1907	m	1921	f	1936	A
1908	n	1922	g	Geo. VI	
1909	o	1923	h	1937	B
Geo V 1910	p	1924	i	1938	C
1911	q	1925	k	1939	D
1912	r	1926	l	1940	E
1913	s	1927	m	1941	F
1914	t	1928	n		
1915	u	1929	o		
		1930	p		
		1931	q		
		1932	r		

Pirates	1909
A Fish Story	1910
A State Governor	1911
Tam o'Shanter	1911
Rob Roy	1912
Crusader	1913
Hooked	1914

COMMEMORATIVE PIECES

Some pieces were made for a special occasion and are dated by reason of that.

Sporting Squire flask with Coronation medallion 1911

Here's a Health Unto His Majesty flask Edward VIII/George VI 1936

The Crown Coronation George VI 1937

Captain Phillip Sesquicentenary of N S W 1938

George V jug, tankard & match ball 1911

Just one more aid is the fact that Doulton introduced a YELLOW CIRCLE to the base sometime before 1905 which defines the earliest issues where the backstamp is almost lost in the dark brown glaze.

If in the text I have stated 'issued in 1915' with no other explanation, especially in *Doulton Kingsware Whisky Flasks*, it usually means this has come from a Doulton memo at sometime. Which, as we have seen, is not always a very reliable source. However, we have all these methods of dating and have to keep looking for clues in order to find all the issue dates. I would be very pleased to hear of any alternative dates found in order to complete the picture.

The reverse side of some *Dewars* and *Greenlees* flasks showing the many different letterings.

The base of the *Hooked* flask
The *Tony Weller* flask with *Dewars Imperial*.

77

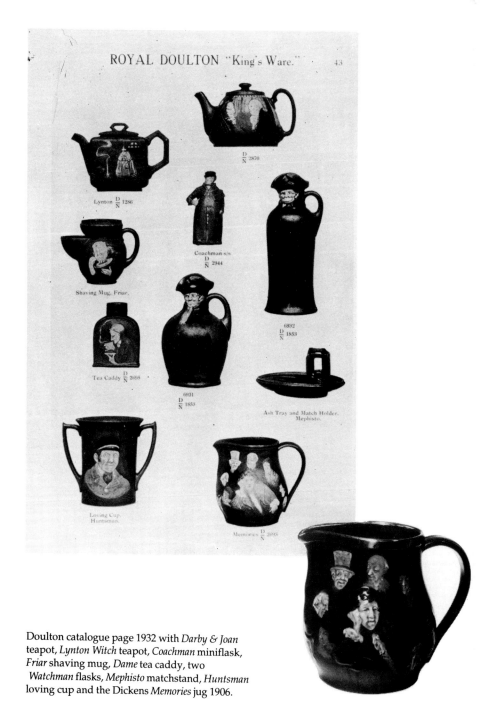

Doulton catalogue page 1932 with *Darby & Joan* teapot, *Lynton Witch* teapot, *Coachman* miniflask, *Friar* shaving mug, *Dame* tea caddy, two *Watchman* flasks, *Mephisto* matchstand, *Huntsman* loving cup and the Dickens *Memories* jug 1906.

ROYAL DOULTON POTTERIES
(DOULTON & CO. LIMITED)
Head Offices: Lambeth, London, S.E.1; Showrooms: Albert Embt., S.E.11

JUGS, ASH-POTS, INK POTS, TOBACCO JARS, &c., IN
NEW DESIGNS OF TOBY FIGURES IN DOULTON LAMBETH STONEWARE.

Royal Doulton catalogue 1927

HARRY SIMEON 1896-1936 studied sculpture at Huddersfield School of Art in Yorkshire where, in 1894, he won a scholarship to The Royal College of Art at South Kensington. He joined Doulton at Lambeth in 1896 and worked on the prestigious *Persian* Wares, Garden sculptures, a range of medieval revival pots and particularly appealing slip-cast bibolots introduced in the 1920's. His modelling for slip casting included a range of toby jugs based on the traditional tobies, but with his own very original simplistic interpretation. The moon flask, tobacco jars and squat jugs are particularly ingenious in the way he has fitted the features into a given shape. The reverse of the moon flask for instance showed toby's back view, the whole very cleverly fitted into a roundel. This range, introduced in 1924, was very popular and after being rather unappreciated for years has had a great revival of interest in the 1990's. This list is included because of this renewed interest and to explain its mention in the Australian list on page 62.

There is an article in the RDICC magazine, volume 1 no. 1 by Stephen Nunn which I have borrowed from adding other pieces I have found. I am also indebted to Stephen Mullins for listing pieces in his collection. The variations are numerous and there must be others to add.

You have only to look at *Toby XX, The Squire* and *Honest Measure* from the Burslem range of tobies introduced in 1939 to see how much Harry Simeons revitalised version of the toby jug influenced Harry Fenton's modelling.

Toby XX, smiling and non-smiling tobies.
Toby XX on a stand, smiling toby, *Toby XX* & Squat jug.
Teapot 4.5"

Two inkwells, small toby & tobacco jar 4.5".
Courtesy Phillips.

TOBY JUGS BY HARRY SIMEON

TOBY JUG smiling with flask and glass 8.5". 7". 6". 4.5". 3". SHAPE NO 8572/89

TOBY JUG non smiling with flask and glass 8.5". 7". 6". 4.5". 3". 8373

TOBY JUG non smiling with flask and glass salt glaze version 6".

TOBY JUG with glass jug, and moulded buttons 3" 8599

TOBY JUG squat shape 4". 2".

TOBY XX Jug. Periwig forms handle. 8". 7". 8589/90/92

TOBY XX Jug. Handle. Salt glaze versions. 14". 10". 8.5"

TOBY XX No handle. 6". 8591

TOBY XX No handle. Salt glaze version. 6" 547

TOBY XX on plated stand with spigot and huntingware bucket. 10". 8589

MOON FLASK made for Asprey. Blue flask, silver mounts. 8.5".

SEATED FLASK Hole in hat for cork. 7".

SEATED TOBY Mug in right hand. Doulton call ash pot, 6". 4.5". 2.5". 543. 8586/7

TOBACCO JAR with tankard and pipe. 5". 8593
TOBACCO JAR smoking pipe. 5".

CANDLESTICK 4".

ASHTRAY AND MATCHHOLDER 2.5".

COVERED JAR hat forms cover. 4". 3".

INKWELL head forms cover. 2.75". 8583/4

TEAPOT (Doulton's first figurative teapot). 4.5".

TOBY JUG smiling. 4.5". Found overprinted, souvenir from *Ye Olde Kings Head, Aylesbury.*

SEATED TOBY 6". Found overprinted, *Ye Olde Cock Tavern*, 22 Fleet, founded 1549. 8543

BEFORE & AFTER MARRIAGE Character Jug, 5", 3.5", 2". 5595/6

The colour variations are innumerable. The coat is found in brown, blue and ivory. The waistcoat in brown, vermilion, olive and ivory. The hat in brown, blue and olive. The breeches in brown and olive. There will be others.

Toby flask 7", serious Toby 8.5", covered jar 4". *Courtesy Phillips.*

Two tobies - one a salt-glaze version.

Moonflask 9.5", Toby jugs 8.5" & 7", squat Toby 6".

INDEX

Photographic Credits
Royal Doulton 6,10,66-70
John Dewar 14
Alan Blakeman 46,48
Mike Bithell 42,59
Gerald Foxwell 29,39

Doulton Kingsware Whisky Flasks.
Paperback, over 70 flasks illus.

£3 + 50p p & p

Doulton Flambé Animals.
Paperback, over 100 animals illustrated, 7 colour pages.

£3 + 50p p & p

Collecting Royal Doulton Character & Toby Jugs.
Hardback, all jugs in colour.

£18 + £1 p & p

Collecting Doulton Animals.
Hardback, 300 animals illus, 10 colour pages.

£12 + £1 p & p

£6 + 50p p & p

Doulton Burslem Advertising Wares.
Paperback, 200 items illus.

Doulton Lambeth Advertising Wares.
Hardback. 192 Pages. 300 B&W illus. 10 colour pages.

£15 + £1 p & p

All available from JOCELYN LUKINS, 14 KEITH GROVE, LONDON W12 9EZ
Also sales lists of Figurines, Character Jugs, Advertising Wares etc.

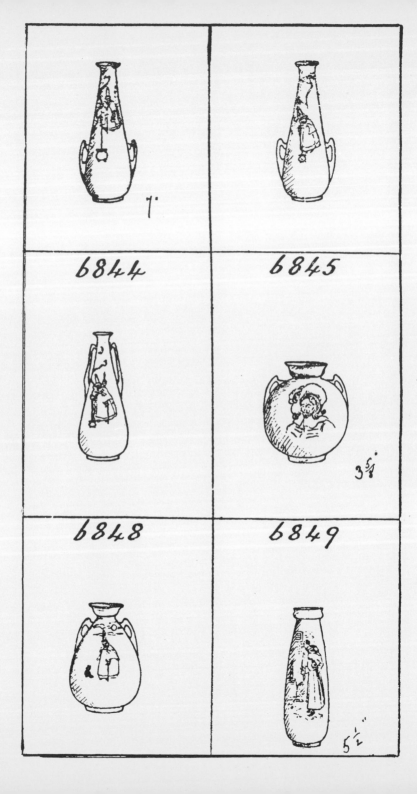

6844

6845

6848

6849